MICRO INTERFACING CIRCUITS

BOOK 1

OTHER BOOKS BY R. A. PENFOLD

MICRO INTERFACING CIRCUITS

BOOK 1

by
R. A. PENFOLD

BERNARD BABANI (publishing) LTD
THE GRAMPIANS
SHEPHERDS BUSH ROAD
LONDON W6 7NF
ENGLAND

PLEASE NOTE

Although every care has been taken with the production of this book to ensure that any projects, designs, modifications and/or programs etc. contained herein, operate in a corrrect and safe manner and also that any components specified are normally available in Great Britain, the Publishers do not accept responsibility in any way for the failure, including fault in design, of any project, design, modification or program to work correctly or to cause damage to any other equipment that it may be connected to or used in conjunction with, or in respect of any other damage or injury that may be so caused, nor do the Publishers accept responsibility in any way for the failure to obtain specified components.

Notice is also given that if equipment that is still under warranty is modified in any way or used or connected with home-built equipment then that warranty may be void.

© 1984 BERNARD BABANI (publishing) LTD

First Published — May 1984
Reprinted — November 1990

British Cataloguing in Publication Data
Penfold, R. A.
  Micro interfacing circuits. — (BP130)
  Book 1
  1. Microcomputers   2. Interfaces
  I. Title
  001.64'04   TK7888.3
  ISBN 0 85934 105 4

Printed and Bound in Great Britain by Cox & Wyman Ltd, Reading

PREFACE

Although the use of computers in measurement and control systems was until recently something only for professional users and a few dedicated amateurs, the falling cost and increasing sophistication of home-microcomputers has changed this completely. It is now perfectly feasible for the average amateur electronics enthusiast to build reasonably simple add-ons for a microcomputer that will transform it into a versatile and sophisticated piece of control and measurement apparatus. Areas of electronics (such as automatic test gear and sophisticated robotics) which were once beyond the reach of most amateurs are now quite commonplace.

Methods of interfacing add-ons to home-computers are not unduly difficult, but for those who are unaccustomed to microprocessor techniques it is easy to be put off by the plethora of unfamiliar terms and devices. The aim of this book is to help those who have some previous knowledge of electronics, but not necessarily an extensive knowledge, to understand the basic principles of interfacing circuits to microprocessor equipment. The subject is not treated in a purely theoretical manner, and the circuits which are used to demonstrate these principles are all practical ones using real devices. The subjects covered include address decoding, parallel and serial interfacing, digital to analogue, and analogue to digital converters, etc. No previous knowledge of microprocessors is assumed.

R.A.Penfold

CONTENTS

Chapter 1

ADDRESS DECODING

In order to understand the basics of microcomputer interfacing it is necessary to have at least a rough idea of the way in
which a microcomputer operates. At this stage, an under-
standing of the arrangement outlined in the block diagram of
Figure 1 is sufficient.

The microprocessor unit (MPU) obtains instructions and
data from the memory, and the address bus is used to select
memory locations. Most microprocessors in common use in
home-computers have sixteen address lines in the address bus,
and like ordinary logic circuits, each of these lines can either
be at logic 1 (high, or at roughly the positive supply voltage)
or logic 0 (low, or at roughly the negative supply potential).
The address lines are named A0, A1, A2, etc., through to A15.
Each address line represents 0 when it is low, or some other
number when it is high, in standard binary fashion. For those
who are not familiar with the binary numbering system the
table below shows the number that each address line represents when it is at the high logic state.

A0	1	A8	256
A1	2	A9	512
A2	4	A10	1024
A3	8	A11	2048
A4	16	A12	4096
A5	32	A13	8192
A6	64	A14	16384
A7	128	A15	32768

Any number from 0 (with all lines low) to 65535 (all lines
high) can be represented using the appropriate set of logic
levels on the address bus, and this enables up to 65536 memory
locations to be addressed. However, not all memory locations
are necessarily used, and with some simple and inexpensive
machines only a very limited amount of memory is fitted.
With the more sophisticated and expensive machines it is

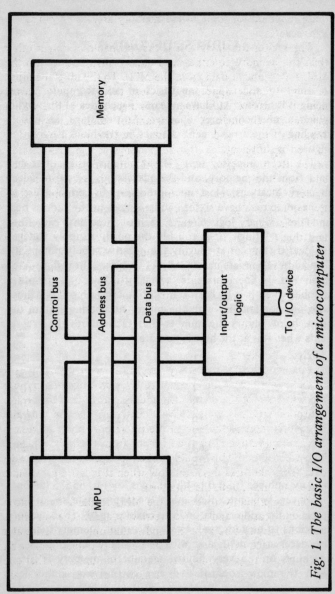

Fig. 1. The basic I/O arrangement of a microcomputer

quite common for some of the memory area to be purposely left vacant.

The reason for doing this is that it enables a circuit other than the memory to either feed data or instructions into the MPU, or to obtain data from the MPU. To the MPU the input or output device appears to be just the same as a normal memory location. Most home-computers are supplied with a manual which includes a diagram or table known as a "memory map", and this shows how the memory area is divided up into sections for such things as the BASIC interpreter ROM, program storage RAM, internal in/out devices, and, hopefully, a spare area suitable for external input/output devices. This method of getting information into and out of the MPU is known as "memory mapped input/output".

The information is carried between the MPU and memory, and the MPU and input/output devices, by way of the data bus. There are currently a number of MPUs which have a sixteen bit data bus, but the ones used in home-computers are almost invariably 8 bit types. The data lines are called D0, D1, D2, etc., and in the same way that the 16 bit address bus can represent numbers from 0 to 65535, an 8 bit data bus can represent numbers from 0 to 255.

Tristate Outputs

The control bus is not really very aptly named, and it is a collection of lines which do not really work together in quite the same way as the lines of the address bus or data bus. It is a collection of lines which have their own function, and the most important of these from the interfacing point of view is the read/write line. This is an output from the MPU which is high when the MPU is reading (when it expects to be fed with data from the data bus), and low when it is writing (when it places an output onto the data bus).

This is primarily to enable the MPU to place data into a memory location, and then to retrieve it again. The important point which must be kept in mind is that only one device at a time can place data onto the data bus. If two devices place an output onto the data bus it is possible (but unlikely) that one or both of them will become damaged, and virtually certain

3

that the data on the bus will be corrupted and that the system will not function properly. The read/write line is used to control the memory and input devices to ensure that they do not place a signal onto the data bus while the MPU is doing so.

In order to achieve this, all devices which place an output on the data bus must have tristate outputs. Apart from normal high and low logic levels, these have a third state where the output is disabled. It is then at a high impedance, and is simply taken to whatever state some other output device places on the data bus. To the device placing its output onto the data bus a disabled tristate output appears to be, more or less, an input. The read/write line, if used correctly, merely ensures that neither memory or an input/output device place an output onto the data bus while the MPU is doing so. Correct decoding of the address lines must be used to prevent more than one memory or input/output device from placing an output onto the data bus at any one time.

In/Out Mapping

Memory mapping is the system used with the 6800 microprocessor, and microprocessors which have been developed from this device. These include the 6802, the 6809, and the 6502. The latter is very popular for home-computer use, and is to be found in several popular machines. Memory mapped input/output is consequently a common system which is much used in home-micros.

However, there is another system which is also much used, and this is input/output mapping. There seems to be a popular belief that this is a totally different concept to memory mapped input/output, but it is really just a variation on this system. Input/output mapping was used on an early microprocessor called the 8008, and it has been retained on more recent devices which have been developed from it. These include the 8085 and the Z80. The Z80 is another device which is much used in home-computers, and input/output mapping is therefore in common use.

The only difference between memory mapping and input/output mapping is that the latter uses two additional control lines. These are the MEMRQ (memory request) and IOREQ

4

(input/output request) lines. These are normally high, but the MEMRQ line goes low when the MPU tries to send data to or receive data from a memory device. The IOREQ line similarly goes low when the MPU wishes to communicate with an input/output device. This enables each address to be used twice, once for memory and once for an input/output device, and permits a full 64k of memory to be used. Although a full 64k of input/output addresses is also available, in practice it is highly unlikely that such a large number of input and output devices would be used. However, as we shall see later, this enables simplified address decoding to be used where only a small number of input/output devices (including any internal ones of the computer) are used.

It is perhaps worth mentioning that it is not essential to use input/output mapping with an MPU such as the Z80, and if there are spare memory locations available it is usually perfectly possible to use these for input/output devices. In some cases this may well be the best way of doing things. For example, the highly popular *Sinclair ZX81* computer has BASIC PEEK and POKE commands that can be used to read from and write to memory respectively. It does not have BASIC IN and OUT commands, and can only read or write to an input/output mapped device using a machine code routine. Not surprisingly, most of the many published add-ons for this computer use memory mapped input and output devices.

Another difference between the 6800 series of MPUs and those in the 8008 family is the use of separate read (RD) and write (WR) lines on those in the 8008 family. The appropriate line goes low when the MPU is reading or writing.

Gates

A simple input port for a microcomputer would normally use an arrangement something along the lines of the one shown in the block diagram of Figure 2. The octal tristate buffer is simply a device which has eight inputs and eight outputs. With the CE (chip enable) at one logic level (usually high) the outputs are at a high impedance and the device is inactive. With the CE (chip enable) input taken to the other logic state each output assumes the same state as the corresponding input, and

5

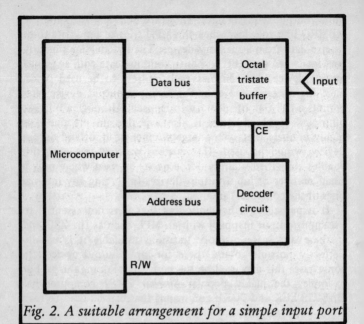

Fig. 2. A suitable arrangement for a simple input port

the input signal is fed through to the data bus.

The decoder circuit must produce a suitable pulse for the CE input of the tristate buffer when the appropriate address is present on the address bus, and when the read/write line is high (in the read mode). For a microprocessor based on a Z80 or similar microprocessor the RD line that would be used instead of the R/W line, and the decoder would have to supply the chip enable pulse when this line was low. There would also be the IOREQ or MEMRQ line to be decoded as well (depending on the input/output system used), and the chip enable pulse would only have to be produced when the appropriate one of these lines was low.

This gives a considerable number of lines to be decoded, with some 17 or 18 to contend with.

It is not always necessary to decode all the address lines. There may well be a few hundred addresses set aside for external add-ons, but you may only wish to add a single device. Some of the lower address lines can then be ignored. If A0 is unused there will be two addresses that will activate the input port, if A0 and A1 are ignored this is increased to four addresses, ignoring A2 as well boosts this to eight addresses, and so on.

Some computers helpfully have an address area set aside for external add-ons, and have a line which goes low if any address in that range appears on the address bus. This internal decoding of the upper address lines avoids the need for any external decoding of them. If only a single port is required it is not necessary to decode the lower address lines either, but it will probably be necessary to have a small amount of logic circuitry as there are likely to be lines such as the IOREQ or R/W which cannot just be ignored.

The most simple of the devices that can be used for decoding are the various types of gate. These have two or more inputs and a single output. There are four main types of gate, AND, NAND, OR, and NOR. Whether the output takes up the high or low logic state depends on the states of the inputs, and on the type of gate used. If we consider the AND type first, the output goes high only if all the inputs are at the high state. In other words, for a two input AND gate, input 1 *and* input 2 must be high in order to give a high output. When first dealing with gates it can be useful to draw a "truth table", such as the one for a 3 input AND gate which is given below.

INPUT 1	INPUT 2	INPUT 3	OUTPUT
LOW	LOW	LOW	LOW
HIGH	LOW	LOW	LOW
LOW	HIGH	LOW	LOW
HIGH	HIGH	LOW	LOW
LOW	LOW	HIGH	LOW
HIGH	LOW	HIGH	LOW
LOW	HIGH	HIGH	LOW
HIGH	HIGH	HIGH	HIGH

A NAND gate is similar to an AND type, but the output only goes low (rather than high) if all the inputs are high. If the truth table for a 3 input NAND gate was listed out it would be similar to the 3 input AND truth table given above,

7

but the output states would be the opposite of those given above.

An OR gate has an output which is high if any of the inputs are high. Thus, for a 2 input OR gate the output is high if input 1 OR input 2 is high. The truth table for a 3 input OR gate is given below.

INPUT 1	INPUT 2	INPUT 3	OUTPUT
LOW	LOW	LOW	LOW
HIGH	LOW	LOW	HIGH
LOW	HIGH	LOW	HIGH
HIGH	HIGH	LOW	HIGH
LOW	LOW	HIGH	HIGH
HIGH	LOW	HIGH	HIGH
LOW	HIGH	HIGH	HIGH
HIGH	HIGH	HIGH	HIGH

A NOR gate has an output which is low if any of the inputs are high. A NOR gate is effectively an OR gate having its output inverted, and its output state is the opposite of what would be obtained using an OR gate.

Practical Gates

Most computers are compatible with the 74** and 74LS** series of logic devices, and these devices are the ones that are normally used in external interfaces. The 74LS** series are the most suitable as they load the outputs of the computer less heavily, take less power, and operate somewhat faster than the standard 74** series of devices. Apart from these differences a 74LS** device is the same as a 74** device having the corresponding number (e.g. a 74LS00 is a pin for pin equivalent to the 7400).

There are numerous gates in the 74** and 74LS** families, and data books giving pin-out details of these are readily available. Some of the larger mail order component catalogues give a lot of useful information on these devices, including pin-out details. Figure 3 gives pin-out information for the gates which I have found to be most useful for address and control line decoding. Often an inverter stage is needed, and the 74LS04 or 74LS14 (inverting Schmitt Trigger) are then useful.

8

Pin-out details of these are included in Figure 3. It is useful to bear in mind that a NAND or NOR gate can be used as an inverter. One way of doing this is to simply connect all the inputs together, but remember that if (say) a 3 input gate is used in this way, the driving circuit is loaded by three inputs and not one. An alternative method which loads the driving circuit with just one input is to connect all but one of the inputs of a NAND gate to the positive supply, or all but one input of a NOR gate to the negative supply. In both cases the remaining input is used as the input of the inverter.

Decoders

There are logic devices which are specifically intended for decoding applications, and one of the most useful of these is the 74LS138, 3 to 8 line decoder. Pin-out details of this device are given in Figure 4.

This has three address inputs called A0, A1, and A2, and eight outputs which are numbered from 0 to 7. One of these outputs, and only one of these outputs, goes to the low state, and it is the binary number fed to the address inputs that determines which output this is. For example, if A0 plus A1 are high and A2 is low, this represents 3 in the ordinary decimal numbering system $(1 + 2 + 0 = 3)$ and output 3 is the one that goes low.

There are a number of advantages to using a decoder rather than gates, and one of these is that no matter what three states the inputs must be in when a low output state is required, one of the outputs must be suitable. Another advantage is that in circuits where several input/output circuits are used, each output of the 74LS138 can be used to enable an input/output device, and a single 74LS138 can replace numerous gates.

A third advantage is that the 74LS138 has an enable input at pin 6, and negative enable inputs at pins 4 and 5. The device will only function properly if pin 6 is taken to the positive supply, and pin 4 plus pin 5 are taken to the negative supply. Otherwise the outputs all go to the high state. In practice this means that the enable and negative enable inputs can be used to decode more inputs, and a 74LS138 can be used to decode up to six inputs. For instance, suppose that we wish to enable

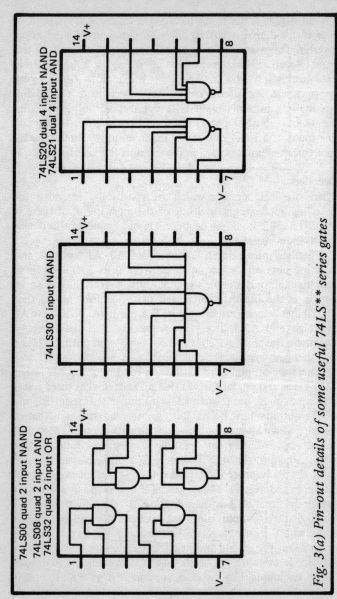

Fig. 3(a) Pin-out details of some useful 74LS** series gates

10

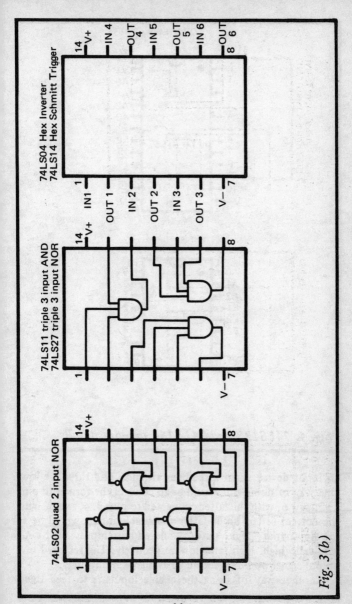

Fig. 3(b)

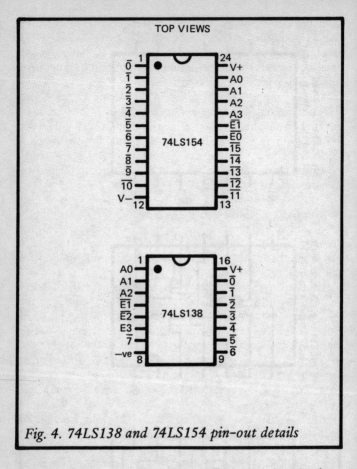

Fig. 4. 74LS138 and 74LS154 pin-out details

an input device when three lines are high, and three are low. One way of doing this would be to connect the former to pins 1, 2, and 6, with the latter connected to pins 3, 4, and 5. With the correct set of input levels the enable inputs would be at the appropriate logic states, while address inputs A0 to A3 would be high, high, and low respectively. The required low output signal would therefore be available at output 3.

Another way of using the enable inputs is to feed them

12

from the output of gates or other decoders that are used to decode additional address or control lines. This can avoid having to use an extra gate to decode these outputs, giving a small but useful reduction in current consumption, component count, and cost.

Another useful decoder is the 74LS154, and Figure 4 also gives pin-out details of this device. It is a 4 to 16 line decoder, but it only has the two negative enable inputs, and unlike the 74LS138, there is no positive enable input. Even so, it is a somewhat more versatile device, but it is larger and more expensive than the 74LS138, and it is advisable to use the latter where this is possible.

Magnitude Comparator

A magnitude comparator is another versatile device for decoding purposes, and the 74LS85, 4 bit type is often used in this application. Figure 5 shows the pin-out configuration for this device.

There are two sets of binary inputs, one set marked A0 to A3, and the other marked B0 to B3. The device compares the two binary numbers fed to these, and the outputs at pins 2 to 7 take up states that depend on whether the number fed to input A is the larger, the smaller, or equal to the number fed to input B. For decoding purposes it is the two outputs that respond to equal inputs that are of interest. The one at pin 3 goes negative if the two inputs are equal, while the one at pin 6 goes positive.

When used for decoding purposes the four lines to be decoded would be connected to the A inputs. Suppose that we require a negative output pulse only when A0 to A2 are high and A3 is low. All that we have to do is connect inputs B0 to B2 to the positive supply rail, B3 to the negative supply rail, and take the output signal from pin 3. The latter will only go low when the two sets of inputs are equal, and this only occurs with the required high – high – high – low input pattern.

As will probably be apparent to you, the B inputs can be programmed to produce an output at pins 3 and 6 for any combination of input levels at the A inputs. It is just a matter of setting the B inputs at some states you wish to decode at

13

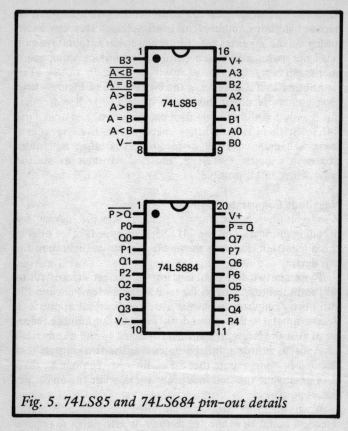

Fig. 5. 74LS85 and 74LS684 pin-out details

the A inputs. Using a circuit based on four 74LS85s it would in fact be possible to fully decode a 16 bit address bus, with the circuit being programmed to decode any of the 65536 possible addresses!

Although we have been assuming that the inputs to be decoded are connected to the A inputs, while the B inputs are set to the appropriate states, the device will, of course, function just as well with the A and B inputs swopped over.

There is an 8 bit magnitude comparator in the 74LS** series of devices, and this is the 74LS684. The pin-out configuration of this device is also shown in Figure 5. With this device a negative output signal is produced at pin 19 when the pattern on the P inputs is identical to that on the Q inputs. This is a very versatile and useful device, but unfortunately it is rather expensive and relatively difficult to obtain. Two 74LS85s plus a 2 input gate to combine the outputs is therefore a more practical choice.

In Practice

As a simple example of how decoding can be achieved using the devices described earlier, let us assume that we wish to decode a R/W line in the read (high) state, plus sixteen address lines when they have the address shown below:

```
A0 A1 A2 A3 A4 A5 A6 A7 A8 A9 A10 A11 A12 A13 A14 A15
 0  0  1  1  1  1  1  1  0  1  1   0   1   1   1   0
```

There are many ways in which this can be achieved, and some are more simple and inexpensive than others. Gates are very inexpensive devices, and often represent the cheapest way of providing suitable decoding, but they are not necessarily the most simple and convenient in use. The choice of components (as with most design work) is often a compromise between cost and convenience. You may also be influenced, quite reasonably, by the fact that you have components in the "junk box" which you wish to use if possible.

Where it is possible to do so, I normally employ an 8 input gate as this decodes a substantial number of inputs at minimal cost and difficulty. In this case we have a number of address lines (plus the R/W line) which will be high when the appropriate combination of logic levels are present, and eight of these can be coupled to the inputs of a 74LS30, 8 input NAND gate. This will give a negative output only when all eight inputs are high. The other address lines, plus the R/W line, if this is not handled by the 74LS30, can then be decoded by a couple of 74LS138, 3 to 8 line decoders. Incidentally, two 8 input NAND gates can be used to decode 16 address lines, with lines that will be high when the appropriate address is present being connected direct to an input of a gate. The others connect to a gate input via an inverter, and a gate must be used to combine

15

the outputs of the two 8 input gates. This system can be a bit awkward to implement in practice, and I prefer to use alternatives such as 3 to 8 line decoders.

Figure 6 shows how the required decoding can be achieved using one 74LS30 plus two 74LS138s. Supply connections (including the one to the E3 terminal of IC1 are not shown). One of the 74LS138s (IC1) is used to decode the output of the gate and the other 74LS138, obviating the need for any additional gates or decoders.

In operation the circuit is very simple. With the correct address on the address lines all eight inputs of IC2 go high, and its output goes low, activating the E2 input of IC1. The three address inputs of IC3 go high, the enable inputs are taken to the appropriate states, and a negative output is produced at output 7 of this device. This is used to activate the E1 terminal of IC1. The three address inputs of IC1 are all taken low, and the required (negative) output signal is available at output O of IC1. Of course, if even one of the input lines is at the wrong logic level the correct set of input levels will not be supplied to IC1, and output O will remain in the high logic state.

Hexadecimal

Before trying to work out a suitable method of address and control line decoding it is essential to determine and list out the logic level that each line will take up when the appropriate address and control line states are present. This can be difficult when dealing with addresses in the normal decimal numbering system, and it is difficult or impossible to quickly work out mentally what address line states are produced by (say) address 49250.

There is a logical way of working out this type of problem, but it entails working out the state of each address line, one-by-one, starting with line A15. For example, with address 49250, this number is larger than 32768 (the number represented by A15), and A15 if therefore high. 32768 is then deducted from 49250, which gives 16482. 16482 is larger than 16384 (the number which A14 represents), and A14 is therefore high. 16384 is then deducted from 16482, leaving 98. This number is less than the 8192 represented by A13, and

16

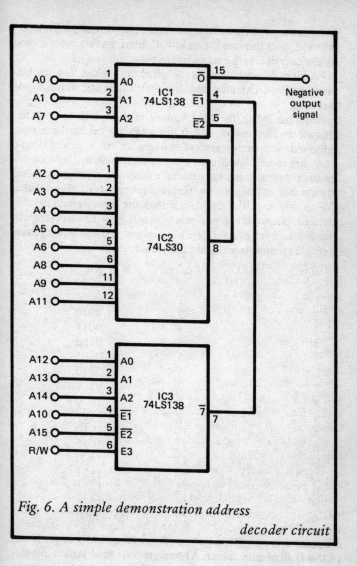

Fig. 6. A simple demonstration address

decoder circuit

A13 is therefore low. It is also less than the 4096 represented by A12, and this line is also low. Continuing this process eventually determines the states of the other address lines.

Addresses could always be given in binary, but working with numbers sixteen digits long with just 1s and 0s is not very practical.

This has led to the use of an alternative numbering system known as "hexadecimal", or just "hex". Whereas the normal (decimal) numbering system is based on ten numbers from 0 to 9, hexadecimal is based on sixteen numbers. As there are not enough numbers in the decimal numbering system, these ten figures are augmented by the first six letters of the alphabet (A to F), and it is from this that the term hexadecimal is derived. The table given below shows how the hexadecimal numbering system operates, by giving some hexadecimal numbers plus their decimal and binary equivalents.

Hex	Decimal	Binary
0	0	0000
1	1	0001
2	2	0010
3	3	0011
4	4	0100
5	5	0101
6	6	0110
7	7	0111
8	8	1000
9	9	1001
A	10	1010
B	11	1011
C	12	1100
D	13	1101
E	14	1110
F	15	1111
10	16	00010000

With this sytem it is quite easy to translate a single hexadecimal digit into the corresponding four binary digits, including the leading zeros, which cannot be ignored in this context as they represent address lines in the low state. Even if you do not memorise the binary group represented by each hexadecimal digit, it is not difficult to mentally work them out when necessary. This is something that could be done with decimal single digit numbers, but it would not be very helpful to do so. What makes hexadecimal numbers so convenient in use is that each digit of the number corresponds to four binary digits, or four address lines in other words. As an example of this, the hexadecimal number A78D can be translated into binary one hexadecimal digit at a time, as demonstrated below:

A	7	8	D
1010	0111	1000	1101

The hexadecimal number A78D is therefore equivalent to 1010011110001101 in binary.

Due to the relative ease with which hexadecimal addresses can be converted into binary, it is advisable to use hexadecimal in preference to decimal whenever possible when dealing with memory or input/output addresses.

Non-Standard Decoding

A point that should be borne in mind when dealing with interfacing a computer, especially when dealing with an unfamiliar machine, is that they do not all utilise standard and straight forward circuits. There are a few machines which use 64k RAM chips, and these represent an economical way of obtaining a large amount of memory. The drawback of doing this and using memory mapped input/output is that there are no gaps left in the address range for any input/output devices! The normal way around this is to deactivate the RAM when an input or output device is addressed so that the RAM does not interfere with it in any way, or vice versa. There will then probably be a pin on the expansion port which can be used by an external add-on to disable the RAM.

The *Sinclair ZX81* computer also has a rather unusual input/output arrangement which is in some ways similar to the system mentioned above. With the *ZX81* the problem is not a large amount of internal memory, but is the less than total address decoding used internally that results in the ROM effectively occupying large sections of the memory space (the so-called "ROM echoes"). The *ZX81* edge connector includes a ROMCS terminal which can be fed with a control signal to disable the internal ROM.

When interfacing to a computer it is therefore necessary to look carefully at the terminals of the expansion port, and find out as much about the machine as you can before attempting to connect any circuit to it. It is advisable not to connect any add-on to a microcomputer unless you are quite sure you fully understand what you are doing.

I mentioned earlier that with input/output mapping it was common for only partial decoding of the address bus to be used, due to only a few internal input/output devices being used, and a full 64k of input/output addresses being vastly more than is normally needed. The *Sinclair ZX Spectrum* is a good example of a home-micro in this category. The basic system used is for the address lines to normally be in the high state, and one of the lower address lines is taken low to activate an internal input/output circuit or a peripheral device. Some of the upper address lines are used to provide additional information to certain input/output circuits.

This leaves some of the middle address lines (5, 6, and 7) free for user add-ons. For a simple input or output port it is only necessary to gate A5 with the IOREQ and RD or WR line (as appropriate) in order to get an enable signal for the chip used to interface to the data bus. Additionally gating A6 and (or) A7 enables more input/output ports to be added.

While this system does not make the most of the input/output possibilities, it does give sufficient versatility for most purposes, it permits ports to be added without the use of any internal address decoding, and little or no external address decoding is required either. Since most users will only need to add a few ports, this represents an adequate and very cost effective solution to the problem.

Chapter 2

INPUT/OUTPUT DEVICES

In the previous chapter methods of decoding the address bus and one or more control lines were discussed. All that this achieves is the production of a pulse each time the appropriate address and control line states are present. This pulse can be used to activate an octal tristate buffer if an input port is required, and the buffer then couples the input signal through to the data bus, and through to the MPU which is reading the data bus at that instant.

A similar process is used where an output port is required, but the tristate buffer is usually replaced by an octal latch. A tristate buffer could be used to connect the output signal (placed on the data bus by the MPU), through to the circuit being controlled by the computer, but this would only give an output signal for the duration of the enable pulse from the decoder circuit. In most applications it is necessary for the eight output lines to be held at whatever state is written to them by the MPU until a fresh set of output states is transmitted. Thus a latching device of some kind must be used.

Where a simple input or output port is required, ports of the type described above are usually the simplest and best way of doing things. Where two or three input or output ports are required, or where versatility is needed, there are special interface devices (known as "parallel interface adaptors", or "PIAs") which are usually a more practical option. The facilities these offer vary considerably from one device to another, but there would typically be two 8 bit ports with each bit individually programmable as an input or an output, plus a couple of handshake lines for each port, and an output to drive an interrupt input of the MPU.

Simple Ports
In this chapter we will consider PIAs, but first some devices suitable for use in simple input and output ports will be described.

21

There are several tristate buffers in the 74LS** series of devices, but the 74LS244 is probably the one which is used most often in this type of application. Figure 7 gives pin-out information for this device.

In normal use as an 8 bit input port the eight outputs of the 74LS244 are coupled to the data bus of the home-computer. These are the terminals called D0, D1, D2 etc. on the computer's expansion port. The eight bit input signal is, of course, coupled to the eight inputs of the 74LS244. There are two negative chip enable inputs on this device (pins 1 and 19), with CE1 controlling buffers 0, 2, 4 and 6, while CE2 controls buffers 1, 3, 5 and 7. When used as an input port for a computer the eight buffers would normally need to be operated simultaneously, and pins 1 and 19 would therefore be connected together. Note that it is a negative control signal which activates the buffers, and a low enable signal which the decoder circuit must supply to the device.

Sometimes less than the full 8 bits of the data bus will be used, with the MPU perhaps just reading the states of three or four mechanical switches. One way of doing this would be to use a 74LS244 and just ignore any unwanted inputs. An alternative is to use a 74LS125 or 74LS126 quad tristate buffer, and these cost somewhat less than the 74LS244. Pin-out details for these are included in Figure 7. The two devices are pin for pin compatable, and the only difference is that the 74LS125 requires a low enable signal, whereas the 74LS126 needs a high enable signal. The control input of each buffer is taken to an individual pin of the device.

A useful alternative to the 74LS244 is the 74LS245 octal tristate transceiver, and Figure 7 also gives pin-out details of this device. This differs from a tristate buffer in that a signal can be fed through the device in either direction. With the send/receive (S/R) input high the input is on the "A" side of the device, and the output is taken from the "B" side. With the send/receive terminal taken low the input is to the "B" side and the output is from the "A" side. There is a negative chip enable input at pin 19, and whichever side of the device is set as the outputs goes to the third (high impedance) logic state unless a suitable enable signal is applied to this.

22

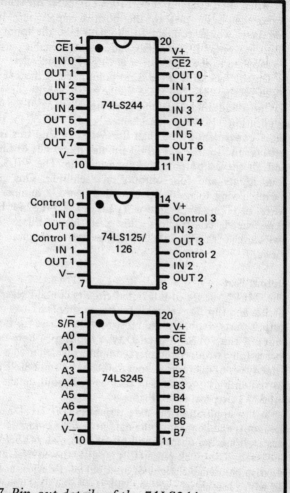

Fig. 7. Pin-out details of the 74LS244,
74LS125/126 and 74LS245

When used as an input port for a computer the send/receive input would be tied to the positive supply rail, the "A" terminals would connect to the data bus, the inputs would connect to the "B" terminals, and a negative enable pulse would be supplied to the CE input at pin 19 by the decoder.

On the face of it there is no point in using the 74LS245 in place of the 74LS244 since the latter is slightly cheaper, and has no disadvantages from the electrical point of view in this application. However, mechanically the 74LS245 is much more convenient in use than the 74LS244, and this is simply because the former has all the inputs on one side of the device and all the outputs on the opposite side. The 74LS244 has four inputs and four outputs on each side. This generally means having to use a double sided board, a number of link wires, or taking tracks between pads of the 74LS244. Even for experienced constructors this can make things a little awkward. With the 74LS245 things are much more straight forward.

Output Port

The 74LS** series of integrated circuits contain several octal latches and flip/flops suitable for use in simple home-computer output ports. Probably the most useful of these for this application is the 74LS273 octal D type flip/flop. I have used this successfully with several microcomputers which used a total of three types of microprocessor (Z80A, 6502 and 6809E), and it proved entirely successful in each case. Pin-out details for the 74LS273 are provided in Figure 8.

In this application the data terminals (D0, D1, D2 etc.) are the inputs and connect to the data bus of the computer. The Q terminals are the outputs and provide normal 74LS TTL output levels. The clock pulse (CP) input is the equivalent of the negative chip enable input of an input port device, and this is fed with a low signal from the address and control line decoder circuit. This signal latches each Q output at whatever logic level is fed to its data input by the MPU at that particular instant. The outputs remain latched at those states until a fresh set of data is written to the port by the MPU. With suitable interfacing (where needed) the port can therefore drive

24

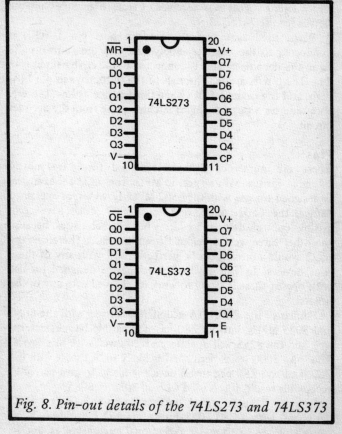

Fig. 8. Pin-out details of the 74LS273 and 74LS373

lamps, motors, relays, etc.

The master reset (MR) terminal at pin 1 is not usually needed in this application, and it is simply connected to the positive supply rail.

Another device which can be useful is the 74LS373 octal transparent latch. When it is in the "transparent" mode this simply acts as eight buffers, with the input logic levels being transmitted through to the outputs. When it is latched, the outputs remain at whatever logic levels they had at the instant

25

the latching signal was received. Figure 8 includes pin-out details for the 74LS373.

When used as a computer output port pin 1 (OE) connected to the negative supply rail; and the control pulse from the decoder circuit is connected to the enable input (pin 11). The inputs are fed through to the output when pin 11 is high, and the device latches when this terminal is low. It therefore requires a positive (high) latching pulse from the decoder circuit.

PIAs

There are numerous PIA devices, and these are mostly intended for use with a specific MPU. The 6522 for example, is designed for use with the 6502 MPU. However, as explained earlier, the 6502, 6800, 6802 and 6809 MPUs have compatible control, data, and address bus characteristics, because the other three were developed from the 6800. Therefore, the 6522 would normally work perfectly well with any of these four devices. In fact any peripheral device designed for use with one of these is likely to work just as well with any of the others!

Similarly, the 8255 PIA is designed for use with the 8080 and 8085 MPUs, but the Z80 has compatible bus characteristics, and the 8255 will operate perfectly well with this device. Thus any 8000 series peripheral is likely to be usable with the Z80, and any Z80 peripheral device is likely to give perfectly acceptable results if it is used with an 8080 or 8085.

In some cases it would be feasible to use (say) a 6502 peripheral with a Z80 MPU, but in practice it would only be worthwhile doing so under exceptional circumstances, and in general it is better to use peripheral interface devices that have reasonable compatibility with the MPU concerned.

6821

For use with the 6502, 6800, 6802 or 6809, the 6821 PIA is probably the best choice if two versatile input/output ports are required, and additional features such as timers are not needed. It has two 8 bit ports with each bit programmable as an input or an output. Each port also has two handshake lines.

26

This is something that will be described in more detail later, but the normal basic function of these lines is to correctly regulate the flow of data into or out of the device. The 6821 has a standard 40 pin DIL package, and the pin-outs are detailed in Figure 9.

Connecting this device to the expansion port of a suitable home-computer is fairly straightforward, but we will consider this in some detail before progressing to how the device is programmed and used. V_{ss} connects to the negative supply rail, while V_{cc} connects to the +5 volt supply rail. When using a simple input or output port based on a few 74LS** devices

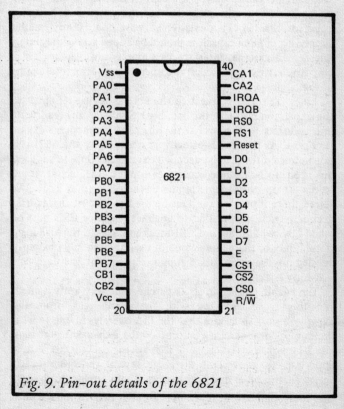

Fig. 9. Pin–out details of the 6821

27

it is usually possible to power the circuit from the 5 volt output of the computer without any difficulty (there is no point in having a supply output if it can't at least power a simple interface). The same is not necessarily true when using a PIA as the total current consumption of the circuit (including address decoding, etc.) is likely to be quite substantial at typically a little over 100 milliamps. Many computers can supply this, but not all are capable of doing so. If in doubt it is better to use a separate power supply for the interface circuit than to risk damaging the computer's power supply. Computers invariably use well stabilised supplies, and if adding an interface circuit causes any significant reduction in the supply voltage this certainly indicates that the power supply unit is being overloaded. Incidentally, at least one 100nF ceramic supply decoupling capacitor should be added across the supply lines of an external interface to suppress noise spikes which could otherwise result in erratic operation or even total failure of the circuit.

Lines D0 to D7 connect to the corresponding terminals of the expansion port (i.e. the data bus). Similarly, the read/write line connects to the read/write line of the computer's expansion port. As this line is effectively decoded by the 6821 it is not necessary for it to be decoded externally. Only the address bus needs to be decoded, and the output of the decoder is fed to one of the chip enable inputs of the 6821 (pins 22 to 24). These three inputs can in fact be used as part of the address decoding circuit. Note that to enable the device CS2 must be taken low, while CS0 and CS1 must be taken to the high logic state. If any of these inputs are not used they should obviously be tied to the appropriate supply rail so that they are permanently enabled.

The enable pin at pin 25 is perhaps not very aptly named, and this is actually fed with the clock signal from the expansion port to ensure that the PIA operates in unison with the computer. The clock output of the expansion port may not be marked as such, and it is often marked "02". It is important to know that there are several versions of each device in the 6800 and 6500 series. These are identical apart from their maximum operating frequency. The basic 6500 and

6800 series can operate with clock frequencies of up to 1MHz, but the devices having an "A" in the type number are high speed 1.5MHz versions. There are also 2MHz versions having a letter "B" added to the type number, and even higher speed versions are becoming available. There is a similar system used with the Z80 series of devices incidentally, but the maximum clock rates for these devices are generally higher than for the 6500 and 6800 series (4MHz for the "A" versions for instance).

In general, if the MPU in the computer is (say) an "A" type device, then the external interface device will need to be an "A" type as well. A faster device could be used for the external interface, but as the cost of the higher speed versions is substantially higher than that of a slower equivalent it would be pointless to do so unless you happen to have a suitable device to hand. One exception to this (and there may well be others) is the BBC computer which has a 2MHz 6502 MPU, but can be used with standard 1MHz peripheral devices. This is made possible by what is effectively a reduced clock speed when an internal or external peripheral device is in use.

The reset input at pin 34 connects to the reset or RST terminal of the computers expansion port. This line is taken low at switch-on by the computer, and this resets all the internal registers of the 6821 to zero. The computer may well have a BREAK key or something of this nature which can be used to reset the machine, and when this is operated it will also reset the 6821.

The RS0 and RS1 pins are register select inputs, and these would normally connect to address lines A0 and A1. This effectively decodes these lines, and they consequently do not need to be decoded by the main address decoding circuit. The 6821 has six internal registers, but as will be explained later, these occupy only four memory locations. The four different addresses that can be fed to the register select inputs is therefore sufficient to enable the MPU to read and write to all six registers. The 6821 will only take up four addresses in the computer's memory map if the register select inputs are fed from the A0 and A1 lines, but if they are fed from other address lines each register will take up several addresses and more of the memory map will be occupied by the interface.

If there is a large block of memory available for external interfaces and you are only using one or two PIAs this would not matter too much, but things are generally more straightforward and less confusing if the circuit is arranged so that the PIA occupies the minimum amount of memory space.

Pins 37 and 38 are the interrupt outputs for the two ports of the device, and these can be connected to the interrupt request (IRQ) input of the expansion port. The basic idea of interrupts is that when one occurs the MPU stops its normal operation, looks to a certain memory location for the beginning of a routine which it then carries out, after which it goes back and carries on from where it left off. This is something which is only needed for a few specialised applications, and as the interrupt routine has to be written in machine code it is something that is strictly for the more experienced computer user. With the 6821 it is possible to inadvertently produce interrupts and "crash" the program if you are not careful, and it is advisable to leave the two IRQ outputs unconnected unless you intend to use interrupts. The two IRQ outputs are driven from open drain transistors, and it is therefore quite safe to connect them direct to each other, giving a sort of simple logic OR action.

The pins marked PA0 to PA7 are the 8 data inputs/outputs of Port A, while those marked PB0 to PB7 are the eight data inputs/outputs of port B. CA1/2 and CB1/2 are the handshake lines for ports A and B respectively. The two ports are almost the same, but there are a few differences.

Using the Ports

The table given in Figure 10 shows how the six registers of the 6821 can be addressed. Of course, just what addresses are used to read and write to the device depends on the address decoding used, but as an example, if address lines A2 to A15 are decoded to place the port between 8000 and 8003, the following would be the result:

8000	Peripheral Register A
8000	Data Direction Register A
8001	Control Register A

8002	Peripheral Register B
8002	Data Direction Register B
8003	Control Register B

It is assumed here that RS0 is connected to A0 and RS1 is connected to A1.

As pointed out previously, there are just four addresses occupied by the port, but there are six internal registers, and consequently two addresses are each used for two registers! One way of doing this successfully is to have one register used only when reading, and the other only used when writing. This is a system used in the 6850 device which we will consider later, but it does not apply in this case as it is necessary to

RS1	RS0	CRA2	Register Selected
0	0	1	Peripheral Register A
0	0	0	Data Direction Register A
0	1	X	Control Register A
RS1	RS0	CRB2	Register Selected
1	0	1	Peripheral Register B
1	0	0	Data Direction Register B
1	1	X	Control Register B

X = Logic state unimportant

Fig. 10. Accessing the six registers of the 6821 PIA

read and write to all six registers. The system that is used here is to have the control register for each port with its own, unshared address. Bit 2 of each control register governs access to the other two registers of each port. With bit 2 of a control register set to 1, access to the peripheral register is obtained, while setting this bit to 0 gives access to the data direction register. Thus in Figure 10 bit 2 of each control register is included, as well as RS0 and RS1.

The names of the registers and their functions can be a little confusing at first, but in use the 6821 is reasonably straight forward. The first thing to do is to set the lines of each port as inputs or outputs, as required. The two ports are set up and used in the same way, and we will only consider port A here. The data direction register A determines which lines of port A are inputs and which are outputs, and this register has to be considered on a bit by bit basis. If bit 7 of the data direction register is set at 1, then PA7 is an output, but if it is set at 0, PA7 in an input. The other seven bits of the data direction register control their respective bits of the port in exactly the same way. The 6821 is normally reset at switch-on by the reset pulse from the computer, and initially all eight lines of both ports are set as inputs. This is really an essential feature since some external circuit might be feeding its outputs to a port, and if the port was to be set as an output at switch-on this would result in two sets of outputs being connected together. However, when dealing with a PIA it is advisable to always set each register at the desired state, and not to assume that the device has been reset properly, just in case a "glitch" occurs at switch-on.

As an example of how port A might be set up for use, let us assume that we want the lower four lines (PA0 to PA3) as inputs, and the upper four lines (PA4 to PA7) as outputs. We will also assume that the port is in the memory map from 8000 to 8003.

The first task is to set bit 2 of the control register at 0 to give access to the data direction register. The port A control register is at 8001, and in BASIC the POKE command (or its equivalent) is used to write to a memory location. Therefore, the first command would be:

32

POKE 8001,0

Then the appropriate figure must be written to the data direction register, and with most computers it is not possible to write numbers to memory in binary. 11110000 in binary is 240 in decimal, or F0 in hexadecimal. The next command would therefore be:

POKE 8000,240

With many computers it is possible to use hexadecimal numbers, and F0 rather than 240 could then be POKEd to address 8000, but remember that a prefix of some kind normally has to be added to inform the computer that the number which follows is in hexadecimal.

This sets up the A port in the required manner, but we now need to be able to read from and write to this port. This is the purpose of the peripheral register A, and this register is effectively port A, but it provides latching on outputs. It is thus possible to drive LEDs, relays, etc. direct from the device, or via just a buffer stage if increased voltage or current drive is needed. In order to gain access to the peripheral register, bit 2 of the control register has to be set at 1. Bit 2 represents 4 when set at the high state, and the following command gives the desired effect:

POKE 8001,4

Again, it would be possible to use hexadecimal with most machines, but in this case the number POKEd would be exactly the same as when using decimal.

Bitwise Operation
It is then possible to write to the port by POKEing the appropriate number to address 8000. Anything written to the lower four bits, which are set as inputs, is simply ignored by the PIA. There is no difficulty in individually controlling each output line. If (say) PA7 is low and you wish to set it to the high state, simply POKEing an additional 128 (the number represented by PA7 when it is high) achieves this. However, in order to do this the number POKEd must be in the form of a

numeric variable. For instance, if the initial number to be sent to the port is 64, it would be sent in this form:

LET X = 64
POKE 8000,X

In order to send PA7 high X would first be incremented by 128, and then X would be POKEd to address 8000, like this.

LET X = X + 128
POKE 8000,X

Reading from the port in BASIC is achieved using the PEEK command (or its equivalent), and the following command would print the returned value on the television or monitor screen:

PRINT PEEK (8000)

This will return a value from every bit of the port, and not just those which are set as inputs. The value returned from bits set as outputs will normally be whatever value was last written to those bits, but if the outputs of port A are heavily loaded so that they are below 2 volts when high, or above 0.8 volts when low, this may not be the case. The value returned from port B outputs is always the value that was written to them, no matter how heavily the outputs are loaded.

It is often necessary to read just one bit of a port, but there is no way of doing this built into a PIA. Instead the logic AND function of the computer must be used to mask the unwanted bits so that only the required bit or bits are read. Most computers have a logic AND function included in their BASIC language, but it should be possible to do this logic ANDing in machine code if there is no BASIC logic AND function.

This AND function works in much the same way as the action of an AND gate. As was described in chapter 1, a 2 input AND gate only provides a high output if both input 1 AND input 2 are high. The logic AND function of a computer compares two numbers bit by bit, and only gives a 1 in the answer if that particular bit of number 1 AND number 2 is a 1. If we only wish to read bit 2 of an input port, the technique is to AND the returned value with whatever number that bit represents when it is high, or 4 in this case. If bit 2 is high the following result is obtained:

```
00000100    Number returned
00000100    Masking number
00000100    Answer
```

If bit 2 is low, this result is obtained:

```
00000000    Number returned
00000100    Masking number
00000000    Answer
```

In both cases the answer obtained is a true reflection of the number returned from bit 2 of the port. The other bits have been assumed to be low and to return a value of 0, but as the following example shows, placing a 1 in some of these bits does not affect the answer.

```
11001100    Number returned
00000100    Masking number
00000100    Answer
```

If a 0 is placed in a bit of the masking number, the result in that bit of the answer can only be 0, and in this way any bits that are not of interest can effectively be eliminated.

Handshaking

Although a computer is not particularly fast by electronic standards, many of the devices which are likely to be coupled to an input or output port are appreciably slower. This generates the need for some means of regulating the flow of data from or into the port, so that the computer is slowed down to a rate that matches the peripheral device. This is the primary function of the handshake lines, although they can be used in other ways.

As a simple example of how a practical handshake arrangement might work, suppose that the computer is being used to operate a simple speech synthesiser. The synthesiser has 256 preprogrammed words which are selected by sending the appropriate numbers on an eight bit data bus. To produce a sentence the computer must send out a string of these word address numbers to the synthesiser, but it must not send a number while the synthesiser is "speaking", only when it has finished a word and is ready for the next one.

There is more than one handshaking arrangement that could be used in a situation of this type, but a typical arrangement would be to have an output terminal on the speech synthesiser which would go high when it is "speaking", and low at other times. This would be fed to a handshake input of the computer. A software loop would be used to hold up the computer and prevent it from sending out a word address when the handshake line was high. When initially sending an address to the synthesiser it would obviously not be "speaking", and the handshake line would be taken low. However, as soon as an address was sent to the synthesiser this line would go high, preventing another address from being sent until the synthesiser had completed the word, and the handshake line was returned to the low state.

With this type of arrangement there is often a handshake output from the computer. A typical way in which this would be used would be for it to give a brief negative pulse (known as a strobe pulse) after each address was sent to the output port. The point of this signal would be to indicate to the synthesiser that the new address was available, and it would be used to trigger the synthesiser into action. An alternative way of using this trigger output is to have it go low when a new address is sent to the port, and to have it reset by the other handshake line going back to the low state at the end of each word.

If we now consider the way in which handshake lines CA1 and CA2 of the 6821 can be set-up and used, the first important point to bear in mind is that CA1 can only be used as an input, whereas CA2 is able to function as an input or an output. Both can be used as inputs to generate interrupt outputs at the IRQA terminal of the 6821, but we will not consider this aspect of their use here. Although the handshake lines cannot handle every handshaking mode, they can be configured to suit practically any application.

If we consider CA1 first, when used as an input it is not its logic state that is important, only transitions from one logic state to another. It can be used to set bit 7 of the control register high on either a low-to-high transition or a high-to-low transition. The mode of operation is controlled by bit 1 of control register A, as detailed below:

CRA bit 1 high   active transition on CA1 is low-to-high
CRA bit 1 low   active transition on CA1 is high-to-low

Whichever mode of operation is used, bit 7 of the control register is reset to the low state by reading peripheral register A.

Three bits of control register A (bits 3, 4 and 5) are used to control CA2. When used as an input it is again transitions from one logic state to another rather than a static logic state that is of importance. It is bit 6 of control register A that is set high by an active transition on CA2. Like CA1, CA2 has two input modes, and these are obtained as shown below:

CRA bit 5	bit 4	bit 3	
0	0	0	Active CA2 transition is high-to-low
0	1	0	Active CA2 transition is low-to-high

The CA2 input flag at bit 6 of control register A is reset by reading the peripheral register.

There are four output modes of CA2, and these are as follows:

CRA bit 5	bit 4	bit 3	
1	0	0	Set high by CA1
1	0	1	Pulse mode
1	1	0	Constant low mode
1	1	1	Constant high mode

In the first mode CA2 is set high by an active transition on CA1, and is set low again by reading port A. In the second mode a brief negative output pulse is produced each time a read operation of port A is carried out. In the constant modes CA2 is simply set permanently high or low. In other words the programmer sets CA1 at the desired state via bit 3 of the control register, and CA2 takes up whatever state is written to this bit of the control register provided bits 4 and 5 are high.

When CB1 and CB2 are employed as inputs they are set-up and used in exactly the same way as the port A handshake lines, but they are, of course, controlled by control register B. There is a slight difference between CA2 and CB2 when they are used as outputs in that when the first mode of operation is used the output is reset by a write operation to the port (not a read operation). Also, when used in the pulse mode the output pulse is produced by a write operation instead of a read operation. In practice this is probably the more useful arrangement.

When reading one of the input flags it is obviously necessary to mask off the other bits of the control register, but this is just a matter of using the logic AND function in the manner described earlier. When writing to the control register to set one of the handshake lines in the desired mode, remember that if you are using the other handshake line you must also set this one up at the same time. If access to the peripheral control register is needed you must also remember to set bit 2 of the control register high at the same time. For instance, suppose that CA1 is to be used in the high-to-low mode, CA2 is to be used in the constant low output mode, and access to the peripheral register is required. The relevant bits of the control register would have to be set-up as shown below:

bit 1	bit 2	bit 3	bit 4	bit 5
0	1	0	1	1

Adding up the total number represented by the bits that are high gives an answer of 52 (in decimal). POKEing this number to control register A therefore gives the desired result.

8255

Although other PIAs are very different to the 6821 in points of detail, the general techniques used are broadly the same. The 8255 offers very different facilities to the 6821, but it uses the same basic technique of a control register to set the ports to operate in the required manner.

Figure 11 shows pin-out details of the 8255. GND connects to the negative supply and V_{cc} connects to the +5 volt supply rail. The data bus, reset, RD, and WR pins simply connect to the corresponding terminals of the computer's expansion port. The negative chip select input at pin 6 is fed with the negative

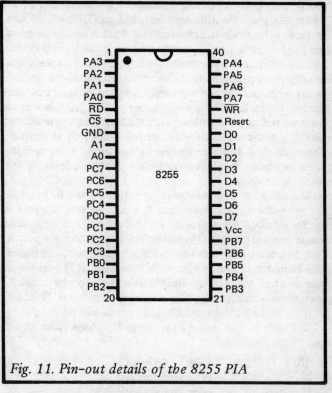

Fig. 11. Pin-out details of the 8255 PIA

output pulse from the address decoder circuit. Note that this circuit must also decode the IOREQ or MEMRQ line, depending on whether the device is placed in the memory map or the input/output map. The 8255 does not require a timing (clock) signal from the computer.

The 8255 has four internal registers, and the required register is selected by placing the appropriate address on address inputs A0 and A1. Where possible these would be fed from the corresponding address lines of the computer's expansion port. The four registers are the peripheral registers for ports A, B and C, plus a control register.

Lines PA0 to PA7 are the port A input/outputs, while PB0

to PB7 and PC0 to PC7 are respectively the port B and port C inputs and outputs. Although, on the face of it, the 8255 with its three 8 bit ports is superior to the 6821 with its two ports, the 8255 is in fact more limited in some respects. This device, like the 6821, has a standard 40 pin DIL plastic package, and in order to accommodate the extra port some of the features of the 6821 such as the handshake lines and interrupt outputs cannot be included. In applications where handshaking is required the usual technique with the 8255 is to have half of port C's terminals as inputs, and the other half as outputs. These are then available for use as handshake lines with the other two ports, but this effectively reduces the device to just two ports.

The 8255 has three modes of operation (Modes 0, 1 and 2), but we will only consider Mode 0 here. In this mode port A can be set as an 8 bit input or an 8 bit output, and mixture of inputs and outputs is not possible. The same is true for port B. Port C is split into two halves (upper and lower), with each half being set as four inputs or outputs. It is possible to have one half set as inputs and the other set as outputs, but all lines in each half of the port must have the same function. Outputs of the 8255 have built-in latches incidentally.

The table shown below gives the address on A0 and A1 for each of the four registers:

A0	A1	Register Selected
0	0	Peripheral Register A
1	0	Peripheral Register B
0	1	Peripheral Register C
1	1	Control Register

Note that it is only possible to write to the control register, and that it is not possible to read its contents.

The three most significant bits of the control register are used to set the mode of operation, and bit 7 is merely set at 1 in order to enable the mode to be selected by writing to bits 5 and 6. If bit 7 is set low the control register functions in a totally different manner, but here we are only concerned with mode 0, and this only uses the control register in its primary form with bit 7 set high. The following table shows how the

40

modes correspond to the states of bits 5 and 6 of the control register.

Bit 5	Bit 6	Operating Mode
0	0	Mode 0
1	0	Mode 1
1 or 0	1	Mode 2

This only sets the mode of port A and the upper section of Port C. The mode for port B and the lower section of port C is set by bit 2, and is mode 1 if this is high, or mode 0 if it is low. There is no mode 2 for these ports. Thus, mode 0 for all three ports is obtained by setting bit 7 high plus bits 2, 5 and 6 low (i.e. writing 128 (decimal) to the control register).

Bits 0, 1, 3 and 4 of the control register control the functions of the three ports, and the table provided below shows how the ports are set-up as inputs or outputs:

Control No.	D4	D3	D1	D0	A	CU	B	CL
128	0	0	0	0	O	O	O	O
129	0	0	0	1	O	O	O	I
136	0	1	0	0	O	I	O	O
137	0	1	0	1	O	I	O	I
130	0	0	1	0	O	O	I	O
131	0	0	1	1	O	O	I	I
138	0	1	1	0	O	I	I	O
139	0	1	1	1	O	I	I	I
144	1	0	0	0	I	O	O	O
145	1	0	0	1	I	O	O	I
152	1	1	0	0	I	I	O	O
153	1	1	0	1	I	O	I	I
146	1	0	1	0	I	O	I	O
147	1	0	1	1	I	O	I	I
154	1	1	1	0	I	I	I	O
155	1	1	1	1	I	I	I	I

As will probably be apparent from this table, bits 4, 3, 1 and 0 respectively control ports A, C upper, B and C lower. A 1 sets a port as an input and a 0 sets it as an output. The control number given in the table is simply the number that must be written to the control regsiter to give the specified input/

output combination, and it includes the 128 that must be used to set bit 7 high and give the correct function from the control register. The control number is, of course, in decimal.

There is insufficient space here to give more detailed information about the 8255, or to provide details of more PIAs, but if you understand the basic way in which the 6821 and 8255 are connected and programmed there should be no difficulty in deciphering the data sheets for these and other PIAs. It is always a good idea to obtain a data sheet for a PIA you intend to use so that you have full information on the device, including such things as input level requirements and output drive capability. A few component retailers sell data sheets for most of their semiconductor range, and the cost is usually quite modest.

Serial Interface

Most home-constructor projects for use with a computer require parallel connection to the machine. In other words, they simultaneously take 8 bits of data from the data bus, or pass data onto this bus 8 bits at a time. Occasionally it is necessary to transmit or receive data in serial form. Here the 8 bits of data are taken from the data bus and placed in a shift register, after which they are sent to the output one bit at a time. When serial data is fed to a computer it is first clocked into a shift register, bit by bit, and then when the full eight bits are present they are passed simultaneously to the computer's data bus.

Common examples of the use of serial data are saving and loading programs on cassette tapes, and communications between computers via modems and the standard telephone lines. In the case of a cassette recorder there is only one recording track used by a normal, inexpensive, portable machine, and the simultaneous recording of eight bits of data is clearly not possible. For communication over some distance it is obviously advantageous to only require two or three connecting leads, rather than nine or more. Also, parallel communication over some distance gives problems with screening the data lines from one another to prevent stray coupling of signals from one line to another. In fact there can be difficulties with parallel communication over distances of more than about 2 metres or so!

Word Format

Practical serial data systems do not normally just transmit and receive straightforward 8 bit blocks of data, and there is a standard single start bit which preceeds each serial data block. There is either one or two stop bits added at the end of each block of data. For data transmission and reception using the standard ASCII (American Standard Code for Information Exchange) system only 7 bits of data are needed, and serial systems using 7 data bits are not uncommon. Sometimes a parity bit is added at the end of a word, and there can be either odd or even parity. With odd parity there is always an odd number of 1s in each word, whereas there is an even number of 1s with even parity. The additional bit is added, where necessary, to change an odd number of 1s to an even number, or vice versa. The purpose of the parity system is to enable a check for errors to be made on received data, with missing or added 1s destroying the parity of a word. However, a double "glitch" could corrupt the word but still leave the correct parity, and this system of checking is not completely reliable. Most serial systems do not use parity checking.

Obviously there are many "standard" serial systems possible, with odd parity, even parity, no parity, 7 or 8 data bits, and one or two stop bits. By far the most common system is the one start bit, 8 data bits, one stop bit, and no parity type, but this system is by no means universal.

The rate at which data is transmitted is a crucial factor, and the transmitting and receiving equipment must be designed to operate at the same rate. If they are not matched reasonably accurately the received data is completely "scrambled", and the system fails totally. There are several standard transmission rates, or "baud" rates as they are called, and the baud rate is simply the number of bits per second that are received and transmitted. There are typically 10 bits in each word (including stop and start bits), and the number of characters per second that are processed is only about one tenth of the baud rate. Some common baud rates are 75, 300, 1200,

2400, 4800 and 9600. It is no coincidence that these figures are multiples of one another. If the clock oscillator of a serial interface is set for a 9600 baud rate, by repeatedly dividing the clock frequency by two it is possible to additionally obtain all the other baud rates.

There are five interconnecting leads in full, bidirectional system. One is merely the earth connection between the two items of equipment, another is the line which takes the transmitted signal, and the third takes the received signal. If data is only being transmitted or received it is obviously possible to dispense with one of the last two lines.

The remaining two lines are handshake lines which regulate the flow of data. These are not always needed, but if (say) a printer is being driven from a serial output, problems can occur when there is a carriage return since this could well take half a second or more. The flow of data must therefore be halted during the carriage return as it cannot be printed and would be lost.

One of these handshake lines is called the "request to send" (RTS) line, or "data terminal ready" (DTR). This is an output which (normally) goes high when the equipment is ready to receive data. The other handshake line is called the "clear to send" (CTS) input, and this prevents transmission of data unless it is fed with a suitable signal from the RTS output of the other item of equipment.

A bidirectional (full duplex) system would therefore be connected in the fashion shown in Figure 12. A system of this type is capable of passing data in both directions simultaneously. If data can only travel in one direction it is known as a "half duplex" system, and this is all that would be required in a simple application such as a printer being fed from a computer.

SIAs
An MPU data bus can be interfaced to a serial data system using TTL devices, but this is doing things the hard way, and there are special integrated circuits for this purpose. There are several types with titles such as universal asyncronous receiver transmitter (UART), serial interface adaptors (SIAs), and com-

44

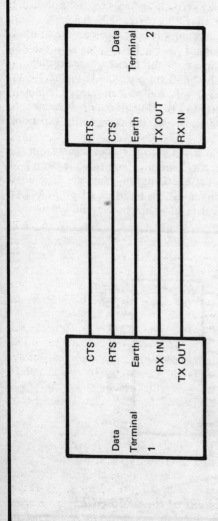

Fig. 12. Connecting two data terminals for full duplex operation

munications interface adaptors (CIAs). There are a number of devices in these categories, but the 6850 SIA is a very popular device for home-constructor circuits. It is quite inexpensive, but it is nevertheless very versatile and easy to use. Although it is designed for use with the 6800, 6802, 6809 and 6502 family of MPUs, with a little ingenuity it is in fact possible to use it with a Z80A based system. As it is far cheaper than the Z80 equivalent it is worthwhile using this device where possible.

Pin-out details of the 6850 are provided in Figure 13. V_{ss} and V_{dd} are the usual 0 volt and +5 volt supply terminals. The data bus, read/write, and IRQ line (if required) connect to their corresponding terminals of the computer's expansion port.

The enable (E) input is fed with the clock signal from the computer's expansion port, and this controls the timing of data transfer between the 6850 and the computer. The 6850 is an asyncronous communications interface adaptor (ACIA), and the flow of serial data does not have to be syncronised

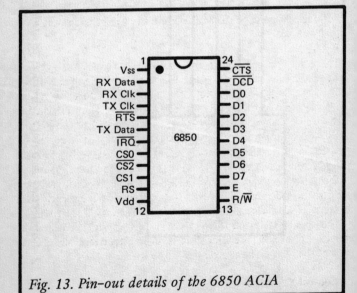

Fig. 13. Pin-out details of the 6850 ACIA

with these transfers of data to the computer. The baud rate is controlled by a clock signal or clock signals connected to the RX Clk (receiver clock) and TX Clk (transmitter clock) terminals. The ability to have different transmit and receive baud rates is useful, but in practice these two terminals would almost invariably be fed with a common clock signal. The 6850 has an internal circuit which, under software control, can divide the clock signal by 1, 16 or 64. We will consider a few simple clock generator circuits later.

RTS and CTS are the request to send and clear to send terminals, and these are active when in the low logic state. DCD is the data carrier detect input, and is used to generate interrupts in automatic systems, but in most applications this input is just tied to the negative supply and the IRQ output is ignored. TX Data and RX Data are the serial output and input respectively.

The three chip select inputs are used in the address decoding circuit, as for a PIA. RS is the register select input, and this is effectively a single address line. This would normally connect to A0 of the computer's expansion port.

In Use

There are four registers in the 6850, two of which are accessed when reading, while the other two are accessed when writing. The two addresses provided by the single address (register select) input are therefore all that is needed. The transmitting register is obtained during a write operation when the RS line is high. The data sent to this register will be transmitted virtually at once if no character is in the process of being transmitted, otherwise it will be sent as soon as the transmission of the previous character has been completed. A read operation with the RS input high reads the contents of the receive data register. A received character is deserialised by a shift register and then transferred to the receive data register, provided the latter is empty. Reading this register effectively clears it so that the next character can be fed to it.

Control Register

The control register is obtained by a write operation when the

RS line is low. Bits 0 and 1 control the division rate for the TX and RX clock signals, as shown below.

CR Bit 1	CR Bit 0	Function
0	0	Divide by 1
0	1	Divide by 16
1	0	Divide by 64
1	1	Reset

Bits 2, 3 and 4 are used to select the desired word format, and there are eight options which will satisfy most requirements. The table below shows the options available:

Bit 4	Bit 3	Bit 2	Word Format
0	0	0	7 bits, even parity, 2 stop bits
0	0	1	7 bits, odd parity, 2 stop bits
0	1	0	7 bits, even parity, 1 stop bit
0	1	1	7 bits, odd parity, 1 stop bit
1	0	0	8 bits, 2 stop bits
1	0	1	8 bits, 1 stop bit
1	1	0	8 bits, even parity, 1 stop bit
1	1	1	8 bits, odd parity, 1 stop bit

Bits 5 to 7 of the control register are concerned with interrupts, and in most cases these can simply be set to a 0.

A read operation with the RS input low returns the contents of the status register. Bits 0 and 1 of this register are the most important. Bit 0 is the receive data register full flag, and is set to 1 when a character has been received and fed to the receive data register. It is likely that characters will be received at a much slower rate than the maximum which the computer can handle. A software loop can be used to read this flag and only permit the data receive register to be read when the flag is high, thus avoiding multiple readings of characters. Reading the receive data register resets this flag, as does a reset. As the 6850 does not have a reset input, and is not reset by the computer at switch-on, this must be done by the user. This is achieved by setting bits 0 and 1 of the control register high (as shown in one of the tables provided earlier).

Bit 1 of the status register goes high if the transmit data register is empty, and the device is ready to receive the next byte of data. A software loop can be used to read this bit and prevent data from being fed to the 6850 until this flag is set to the high state, thus correctly regulating the flow of out-going data. If data is being taken from a source such as a keyboard the flow of data may be too slow for this regulation to be necessary.

If handshaking is being used, bit 3 of the status register is important, and this is set at the same level as the clear to send input of the 6850.

The information provided here is sufficient to enable the 6850 to be fitted into most practical applications for the device, but for more detailed information on the 6850 the relevant data sheet should be consulted. Once you understand the basic principles of serial data transmission, plus the use of control and status registers, there should be no great difficulty in following the data sheet for the 6850 or other serial interface adaptor integrated circuits. The best way to become familiar with complex devices such as ACIAs and PIAs is to gain some practical experience with them.

Clock Oscillator

The clock signals for the 6850 need to be equal to the baud rate, 16 times this rate, or 64 times this rate, depending on the way the internal divider of the device is programmed. In practice it is best to use a divide by 16 or 64 action, as the clock is then internally syncronised with the received data.

The accuracy of the clock frequency needs to be reasonably good, but I have found that a simple C – R clock oscillator of the type shown in Figure 14 is perfectly adequate (for a system using a fairly low baud rate anyway). This is just a simple 555 astable circuit which uses either the standard 555 or the low power 7555 CMOS version. VR1 is used to trim the output frequency to the correct figure, and ideally a frequency counter or some other accurate method of frequency measurement should be used when doing this. Otherwise it is a matter of using trial and error to find a suitable setting.

The specified values give an output frequency of 19.2 kHz, which is suitable for a 300 baud system with the 6850 used in the divide by 64 mode, or 1200 baud if it is set to the divide

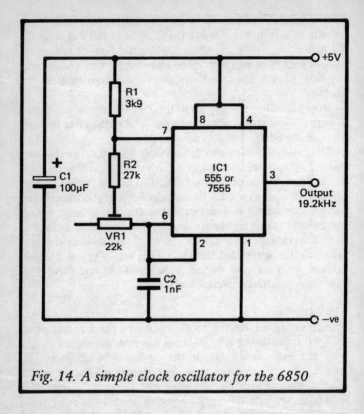

Fig. 14. A simple clock oscillator for the 6850

by 16 mode. This enables two popular baud rates to be accommodated, with the required rate being selected under software control. The output frequency can be changed by altering the value of C2, and the change in output frequency is inversely proportional to the change in C2's value. It is advisable to have C2 no lower than about 100pF in value.

The versatile clock oscillator of Figure 15 uses a CMOS 4060BE crystal oscillator/14 stage binary counter to generate a wide range of output frequencies. These enable practically any normal baud rate to be accommodated. Note that there is no 1.2 kHz output since the 4060BE does not have the output from the 11th divider stage externally accessible. The outputs

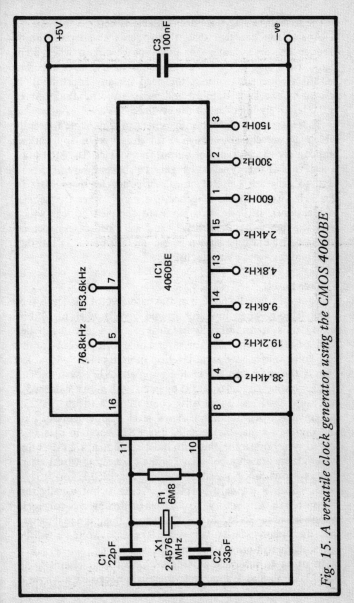

Fig. 15. A versatile clock generator using the CMOS 4060BE

of the first three stages are not available either.

Apart from the fact that it provides a number of output frequencies, an advantage of this type of circuit when compared to a simple C − R oscillator is that it gives accurate output frequencies without the need for any adjustment. It also gives excellent stability and reliability. The disadvantage is the relatively high cost of the crystal.

There are special "bit rate generator" integrated circuits which are specifically designed for this type of application, and can give a vast range of output frequencies. The MC14411 is a device of this type, and Figure 16 shows how this can be used to generate a useful range of frequencies from 75Hz to 9.6 kHz (it is capable of generating many other frequencies incidentally). Bit rate generators are complex devices which tend to be rather expensive, and in most cases a clock generator of the type shown in Figure 15 is perfectly satisfactory, and far more cost effective.

Voltage Levels

The output from the 6850 is at standard 5 volt logic levels (i.e. about 0 volts when low and around 5 volts when high), but serial data systems normally use dual balanced 12 volt supplies with a central earth rail. This gives a high logic level of around +12 volts, and a low logic level of approximately −12 volts. This is the method used in the popular RS232 system. The RS423 system is similar, but it operates with a dual balanced 5 volt supply. This is actually compatible with the RS232 system which has minimum signal level requirements of plus and minus 3 volts. Incidentally, the RS232 system uses a 25 way D type connector, but with most equipment that uses this system there are only between 2 and 5 connecting wires!

It is sometimes possible to drive an RS232 or RS423 system from a standard 5 volt logic circuit, but usually this will not give satisfactory results. When driving a 5 volt logic circuit from an RS232 or RS 423 system there is a real danger that the circuit will be damaged as the input voltages will be well outside its normal operating range.

In order to interface a standard 5 volt logic circuit to an RS232 or similar system it is therefore necessary to have a

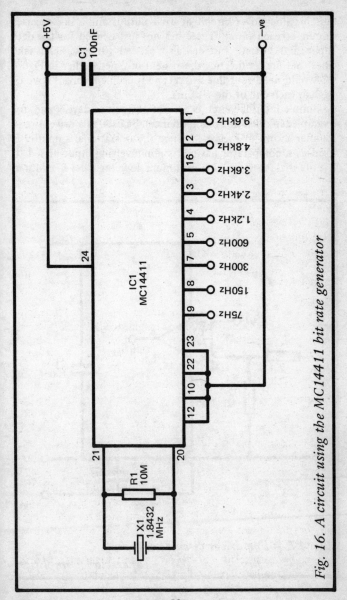

Fig. 16. A circuit using the MC14411 bit rate generator

53

suitable line driver circuit at each output and a line receiver circuit at each input. These are not just needed for the data input and output, but are also needed for any handshake lines that are used. Thus the system outlined earlier in Figure 12 would need four line drivers and four line receivers (two of each at each end of the system).

Simple interface circuits are not difficult to devise, and, for example, an operational amplifier can be used as a driver in the manner shown in Figure 17. Here the operational amplifier is used as a comparator having its non-inverting input biased to a potential between the maximum low logic level and the

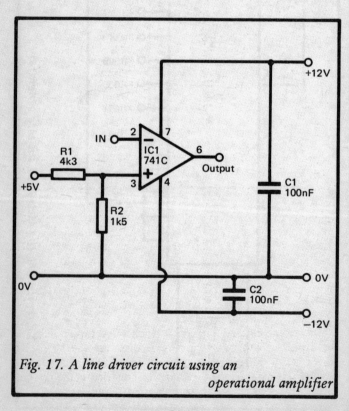

Fig. 17. A line driver circuit using an
operational amplifier

54

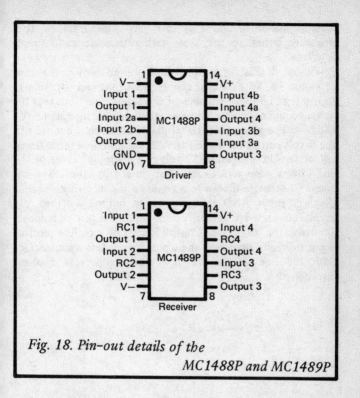

Fig. 18. Pin-out details of the MC1488P and MC1489P

minimum high logic potential. The inverting input is fed with the input signal, and as this switches above and below the reference voltage at the non-inverting input the output switches fully positive and negative. Dual balanced 12 volt supplies are used for IC1 so that a suitable output voltage swing is obtained. As it stands the circuit gives an inverting action, but, if this phase inversion is not required, it can be eliminated by simply swopping over the inputs of IC1.

Driver and receiver integrated circuits for this application are available, and two examples of these are the MC1488P (driver) and MC1489P (receiver). The 75188 and 75189 devices are equivalents to these. Each device contains four drivers or receivers. As these integrated circuits are not particularly expensive and they give very reliable results, it is probably better to use these rather than design a simple interface.

Pin-out details for the MC1488P and MC1489P are shown in Figure 18. Note that the supply pins of the receiver connect to the 0 and +5 volt supplies of the logic circuit, but that the driver requires separate plus and minus 12 volt supplies for V+ and V−. The ground (GND) terminal of the driver connects to the 0 volt earth rail of the logic circuit, and the central 0 volt rail of the dual balanced 12 volt power supply. Three of the line drivers have two inputs, but, internally, these are just taken via separate diodes to a common input, giving a sort of simple 2 input AND arrangement. In normal use these are simply connected together, or one input can just be ignored. Similarly, the "Response Control" input of each line receiver is not normally used, and these pins are just left unconnected. Both the line drivers and line receivers provide a phase inversion.

Chapter 3

PORT INTERFACING

There is more to interfacing a microcomputer than fitting it with an input/output port, or learning how to program the bult-in port if one of these is fitted. In some cases the equipment providing an input signal will provide this signal in a form that can be connected directly to an input port. It is occasionally possible to drive the controlled piece of equipment direct from an output port. However, in most cases it is necessary to have an interface circuit of some kind, and fortunately, this does not usually involve anything particularly complex.

In this chapter we will consider various ways in which electronic equipment can be interfaced to a computer port, and topics such as relay drivers and opto-isolators will be covered.

Relay Drivers
When at the high logic state an output line of a computer port typically gives a little under 5 volts, and the available current is quite low with perhaps less than 10 milliamps available with the output practically short circuited. There are some items of electrical and electronic equipment that can be driven from an output with such low voltage and current drive capability, but there are only a few of these. For example, a light emitting diode requires only around 5 milliamps at a potential of about 2 volts in order to light up reasonably brightly. A LED display can therefore be driven direct from a computer port without any difficulty. Usually a series resistor for each LED is not required as the current is limited to a suitable figure by the current drive capability of the port.

There are miniature reed relays that are housed in what is a sort of tall 14 pin DIL plastic package, and some of these will operate with a coil voltage of as little as 3.7 volts, and a minimum drive current of 7.4 milliamps. These can be driven direct from a TTL output, or an output having similar characteristics (which includes most computer port outputs). A suppressor diode to protect the output against the reverse voltage generated as the relay switches off is built into the relay. While for some applications these relays offer a very simple way of controlling a piece of equipment, the limitations of the relay contacts have to be kept in mind. The maximum current, voltage, and power ratings vary somewhat from one type to another, but none of these components seem to be capable of handling a 240 volt AC mains load. The maximum power that can be handled is usually in the range 3 to 10 watts. This enables loads such as low voltage filament bulbs and small electric motors to be controlled, but is inadequate for the majority of applications.

It is quite easy to boost the output current and voltage drive capability of a port using a simple transistor switch, and Figure 19 shows two simple circuits to do this. The first (a) uses a high gain bipolar transistor as a common emitter switch. The maximum output voltage from a logic output when it is in the high state is about 0.8 volts, and this is sufficient to bias a bipolar transistor hard into conduction. D1 and R2 are therefore used to effectively reduce the output potential from the output port by about 0.6 volts so that Tr1 is switched off when the output is low. When the output goes high it will achieve a potential of 2 volts or more and the potential dropped across D1 is not sufficient to prevent Tr1 from being switched on and activating the relay. R1 provides current limiting, if this should be necessary.

It has been assumed that increased voltage drive is required, and that a separate, higher voltage supply, is used for the relay. However, if a 5 volt supply is adequate to drive the relay, and the computer can provide sufficient output current, the supply for the relay and driver circuit can be obtained from the computer. Bear in mind that about 0.5 volts will be dropped across the collector − emitter terminals of Tr1, and that only about 4.5 volts will be fed to the relay coil.

Even if a higher supply voltage is needed for the relay, many computers seem to have a +9 volt or +12 volt output on their expansion port or at a separate power output socket. Although this supply often has a very high level of ripple and is not stabilised, for an application such as a relay driver circuit

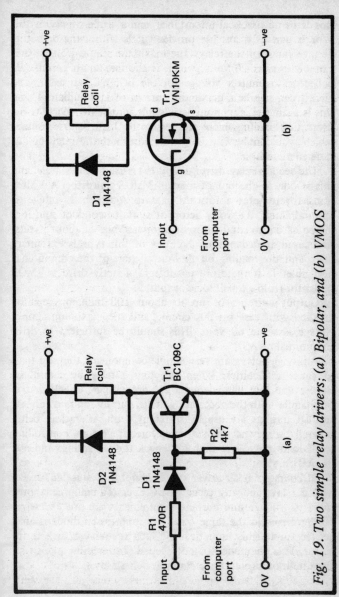

Fig. 19. Two simple relay drivers; (a) Bipolar, and (b) VMOS

this is of no practical importance, and a crude supply of this type is perfectly suitable provided it is within the operating voltage range of the relay. The maximum supply voltage that can be used is 20 volts, which is the maximum permissible collector to emitter voltage for the BC109C transistor. The circuit can handle a maximum current of 100 milliamps, and this is again the maximum permissible for the BC109C. D2 is a protection diode which suppresses the high reverse voltage which would otherwise be generated across the relay coil as it de-energised.

The second relay driver circuit (b) is even more simple, and this is due to the use of a small VMOS transistor. A VMOS transistor requires a forward gate to source bias voltage of approximately 0.8 volts before it starts to conduct, and it is biased hard into conduction by a forward bias of about 5 volts. The input impedance of a device of this type is extremely high, and the loading on the output port of the computer is negligible. It is therefore possible to directly drive a VMOS transistor from a 5 volt logic output.

Output currents of up to about 100 milliamps can be handled with ease by this circuit, and the maximum supply voltage is some 60 volts. This should be sufficient to drive any normal relay.

Although relays are very simple components they do tend to cause difficulties. When selecting a relay be careful to choose one that has adequate contact ratings. Check that it can handle both the necessary voltage, current, and power. AC and DC ratings are usually different, with AC ratings being generally somewhat higher. Therefore, if you are controlling a DC load make sure that you check the DC ratings and not the AC ones!

Of course, a relay driver circuit is not only suitable for use with a relay, and any piece of DC operated equipment, provided its voltage and current requirements are not excessive, can be driven in the same way. The suppression diode is only needed for a highly inductive load such as a relay or an electric motor. This component is not needed if something like a filament bulb or an electronic circuit is being driven.

60

ULN2003

In applications where a number of relay drivers are needed, a relay driver integrated circuit such as the ULN2003 is probably the most practical solution. This has seven Darlington Pair drivers with current limiting resistors in series with each input. It also has a protection diode for each output. Figure 20 shows pin-out details for this device.

In use the negative supply terminal (pin 8) connects to the 0 volt rail of the computer port, as well as to the negative supply rail of the power supply for the relay (if a separate supply is used for the relay). The relays connect between each output and the positive supply rail, while each input connects direct to an output line of the computer port. Any relay drivers that are not needed are just ignored. The positive supply connection of the UNL2003 only connects to the anodes of the protection diodes, and can be left unconnected if the device is used to drive non-inductive loads.

The maximum permissible supply voltage is 50 volts, and currents of up to 500 milliamps can be handled by each driver. However, in order to prevent excessive dissipation and the possible destruction of the device through overheating, it is advisable to keep the current through each driver at no more than about 100 milliamps if all or most of the drivers are used.

For the control of fairly high currents the use of a Darlington power transistor is probably the most practical approach, and Figure 21 shows the circuit of a simple driver of this type. This uses a TIP122 device, and this has a typical current gain of about 5000! The circuit is therefore able to handle currents of up to around 2 amps with a voltage drop of approximately 1 volt across Tr1. It is advisable to fit Tr1 with a small heatsink, and a small, ready-made, finned type is suitable, or a piece of 18 SWG aluminium about 50mm square should suffice. Note that the heat-tab of the TIP122 connects internally to its collector terminal.

About 1.2 volts is needed at the base of a Darlington device before it starts to conduct, and a diode in the base circuit to reduce the input voltage is therefore unnecessary (R1 is for current limiting). This circuit can be used with a maximum supply potential of 100 volts.

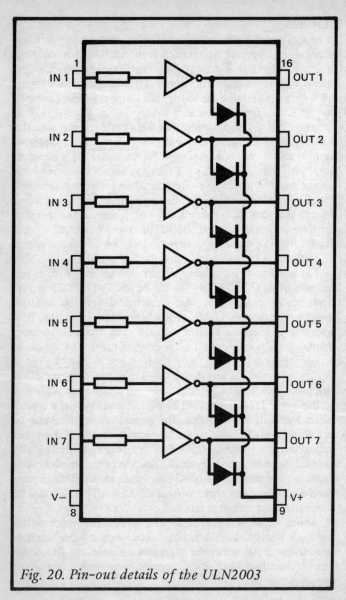

Fig. 20. Pin-out details of the ULN2003

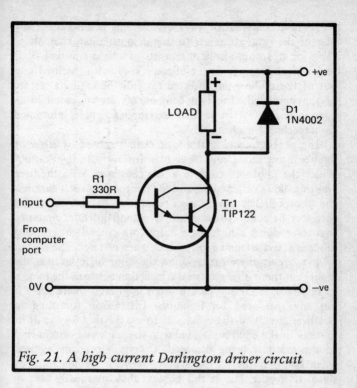

Fig. 21. A high current Darlington driver circuit

Opto-Isolators

An advantage of a relay over a straight forward driver circuit is that it gives total isolation between the computer and the circuit being controlled. With the driver circuit used to operate the load directly, the earth rail of the computer and the earth supply rail of the controlled equipment have to be connected together. Also, only DC powered equipment can be controlled.

A relay has what is effectively just an ordinary switch (operated by an electromagnet) which is not in electrical contact with the driver circuit. It can therefore be used to control AC or DC equipment, and there is no need for any direct connection between the computer and the controlled equipment.

63

There are alternative ways of achieving this isolation, and one of the most simple is to use an opto-isolator circuit of some kind. An opto-isolator consists of a light emitting diode plus a photosensitive device of some kind, with the light output of the diode being directed towards the sensitive surface of the photocell. The two components are mounted in an opaque encapsulation so that extraneous light is prevented from reaching the photocell.

The general idea is that a logic output is used to drive the light emitting diode, and when it is driven on, its light output causes the photocell to have a low resistance. With the light emitting diode switched off and the photocell in total darkness the photocell has a very high resistance. The photocell can therefore be connected in a simple potential divider circuit so that it produces a high logic output when the light emitting diode is activated, and a low output when it is not. The output of the circuit therefore assumes the same logic level as the input, but there is no electrical connection between the two.

Interfaces of this type are often used even where there is not any real need for isolation. The reason for using an isolation circuit in these cases is to ensure that any fault or mistake in the equipment used with the computer cannot lead to the machine being damaged. Opto-isolators can be used when taking outputs from a port, or when feeding an input signal to a port, but in this context they are mostly used in input circuits. Whether this is really worthwhile is doubtful, and really depends on the type of circuit that the computer will be used with, and on whether or not the user is accident prone!

The standard type of opto-isolator uses an infra-red LED plus a photo-transistor. The reason for using an infra-red LED, rather than a normal type having its output in the visible light spectrum, is simply that photosensitive semiconductors mostly have a peak response in the infra-red region. An infra-red LED therefore helps to give peak efficiency from the device.

Figure 22 shows how a TIL111 or similar opto-isolator (such as the IL74) can be used as a simple logic level transfer/ isolator circuit. Here the LED is driven from a logic output in the normal way, with R1 providing current limiting if neces-

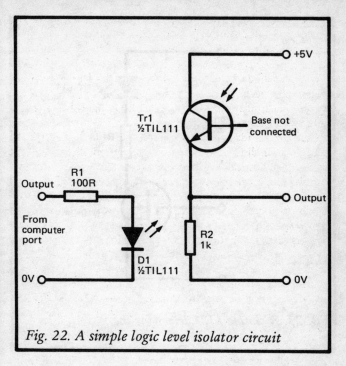

Fig. 22. A simple logic level isolator circuit

sary. The photo-transistor is connected in a potential divider circuit with its collector to emitter resistance forming one element of the divider, and R2 forming the other. The photo-transistor is used as the upper element of the divider so that a high output level is produced when the LED is switched on, and no inversion is produced through the circuit.

Some logic outputs give an inadequate drive current for the LED, and the driver circuit of Figure 23 can then be used to boost the LED current to a suitable figure (about 10 milliamps in fact).

There are dual and quad opto-isolators available, such as the ILD74 (dual) and ILQ74 (quad), and these are generally more convenient and less expensive to use than single types where a number of isolators are required. Figure 24 gives pinout details for single, dual and quad opto-isolators.

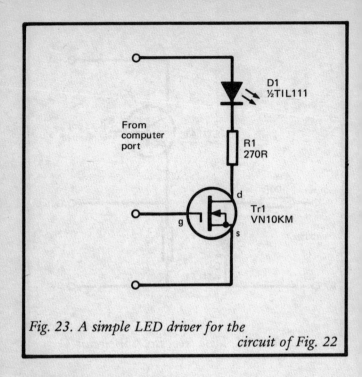

Fig. 23. A simple LED driver for the
circuit of Fig. 22

Triac-Isolator

An ordinary opto-isolator such as the TIL111 or IL74 can only handle fairly low voltages and currents, and is only suitable for use with DC loads. These devices are therefore unable to directly control even a low power mains load. It is possible to use a standard opto-isolator to control a triac, which in turn controls the mains load, but these days there is an easier way of doing things.

This is to use a special type of opto-isolator which is often called a "triac-isolator", and as its name implies, it uses a photosensitive triac instead of a phototransistor. The MOC3020 is an example of a triac-isolator. Figure 25 shows how the MOC3020 can be used to control a small mains load, and also gives pin-out information for this device.

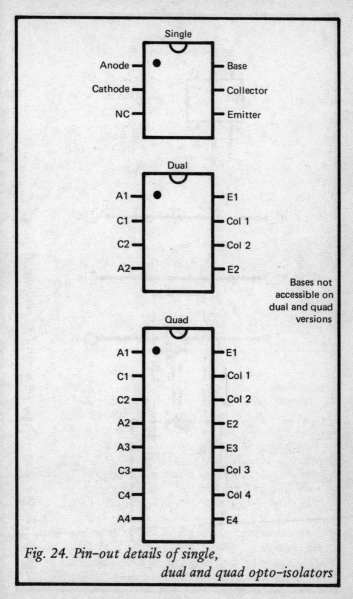

Fig. 24. Pin-out details of single,
dual and quad opto-isolators

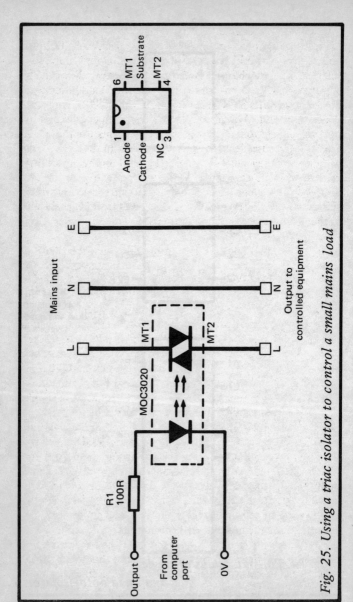

Fig. 25. Using a triac isolator to control a small mains load

In operation the circuit is very straight forward. The LED is fed from the output port in the usual way, using a LED driver if necessary. As a LED current of a few milliamps is quite sufficient to operate the triac-isolator a LED driver is not likely to be needed. A normal triac is triggered into conduction by a forward bias to its gate terminal, but in this case the gate connection is absent. A triac can be triggered into conduction by applying a high voltage across the two "mains terminals". A high voltage causes leakage currents to flow in the device, and these lead to a regenerative action which brings the device into conduction in much the same way as a gate trigger current. Normally the voltage needed to do this is very high, but when the triac section of the isolator is subjected to the light output of the LED strong leakage currents flow with a very low voltage applied to the device.

The triac is therefore switched off when the LED is switched off, but when the latter is activated, the triac breaks down and goes into conduction early in each mains half cycle (it has to retrigger on each half cycle as it switches off at the end of each half cycle when the current through the device falls to zero). This effectively couples the 'L' side of the mains straight through the device to the load, with an insignificant voltage drop of about 1 volt through the triac section of the isolator. As the triac conducts in both directions, and it has no gate terminal, the circuit will work just as well if the MT1 and MT2 terminals are transposed. Note that no connection should be made to the substrate terminal of the triac-isolator.

While the circuit of Figure 25 is very simple and convenient in use, it has a major drawback in that the MOC3020 has a maximum current rating of just 100 milliamps (its PIV is 400 volts incidentally). When used with the 240 volt AC mains supply this enables a load having a power rating of no more than 24 watts to be controlled. This is obviously less than the power rating of most pieces of mains powered equipment, and seriously limits the usefulness of the circuit.

Fortunately, it is an easy matter to use the triac section of the isolator to trigger a higher power triac so that much higher powers can be controlled. Figure 26 shows a simple way of achieving this. The triac part of the isolator is connected so

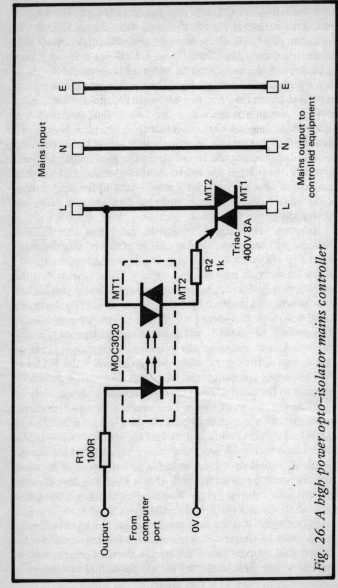

Fig. 26. A high power opto-isolator mains controller

that when it is activated it provides a trigger current for the main triac via current limiting resistor R2. The main triac has a current rating of about 8 or 10 amps, and provided it is mounted on a reasonably large heatsink (about 4.5°C per watt or less) powers of up to about 1500 watts can be controlled. Any normal triac having a current rating of about 8 to 10 amps and a voltage rating of 400 volts is suitable, but a type having a built-in diac is not.

When dealing with the mains supply it is important to construct projects in such a way that there is no exposed mains wiring, or any way in which someone could inadvertently or easily come into contact with any mains wiring. If a metal case or chassis is used this should be earthed to the mains earth lead. Unless you fully understand what you are doing, it is better not to try out this type of circuit until you do. It is not just the project and computer that will be at risk if an error is made when constructing a circuit of this type!

Debouncing

Feeding a signal into a computer is often quite straightforward as in many cases it will be a logic circuit that is supplying the input signal. It is then almost certain that the input can be successfully coupled direct to the input port without any difficulty. Analogue signals are more difficult, and analogue converters are covered in the next chapter.

Another common signal source is a mechanical switch of some kind. This might be a normal (manually operated) type, or perhaps a micro-switch or reed switch. Whatever type of switch is used, a problem which is almost certain to be encountered is the so called "contact bounce". This is where the switch does not make and break "cleanly", but instead produces a number of noise spikes each time it opens or closes. In non-digital applications this is not usually of any significance, but in a digital system it is likely that the circuit will be responding to the number of pulses produced by the switch. To the digital circuit the noise spikes caused by contact bounce are probably going to be indistinguishable from the proper pulses from the switch, and incorrect operation of the system will be caused by the circuit responding to these noise

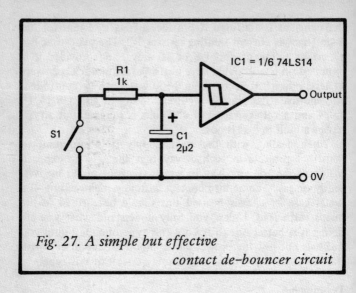

*Fig. 27. A simple but effective
contact de-bouncer circuit*

signals.

There are many ways of eliminating the noise produced by contact bounce, and the circuit of Figure 27 shows one of the more simple but effective ways of doing this. IC1 is one of the six inverting Schmitt Triggers in a 74LS14 device (pin-out details for this were provided earlier in Figure 3). Under stand-by conditions (with S1 open) the input of IC1 goes to the high state, and the output therefore goes low.

If S1 is closed, the input of IC1 is taken low and the output goes high, but R1 and C1 form a simple low pass filter which effectively filters the high frequency noise spikes generated by S1 so that they are prevented from reaching the input of IC1, or are at least greatly attenuated. A Schmitt Trigger has hysteresis, which simply means that it has a reluctance to trigger from one state to the other. This is introduced by having the input voltage at which the output triggers to the high state lower than the input potential at which it triggers back to the low state. Thus, even if a small amount of noise does reach the input of IC1, it will not cause spurious output signals.

72

Ideally C1 should have a fairly high value, such as the suggested one of $2\mu2$. However, a high value tends to slow up the response to S1 closing, and in applications where a fast response time is essential it might be necessary to use a lower value for C1. It is then a matter of finding by empirical means the lowest value for C1 that eliminates contact bounce.

If a negative pulse is needed when the switch is activated it is merely necessary to add an inverting Schmitt Trigger at the output of IC1, and then use the inverted output signal from this device.

Chapter 4

ANALOGUE CONVERTERS

While there are some applications for a microcomputer plus interface that involve only digital signals, most practical measurement and control applications involve analogue signals. A computer deals in binary numbers represented by 5 volt logic signals, but there are few things in the real world (or even the electronic world) which provide or respond to a signal of this type. Measurement of practically anything involves the use of a transducer of some kind which gives output voltage that is proportional to whatever is being measured. This could be a thermistor or temperature sensing semiconductor device in an electronic thermometer circuit, or perhaps a photocell in a light measuring application. Control of something like the speed of an electric motor requires a variable voltage, as the speed of the motor is dependent on the applied voltage.

Obviously there is no way in which a voltage from a sensor circuit can be directly coupled to an 8 bit digital input port, or the speed of an electric motor can be properly controlled by driving it direct from an 8 bit output. In order to feed an input voltage to a computer it must first be processed by an analogue to digital converter, and this is merely a circuit which gives a digital output which is proportional to the input voltage. For instance, if an input voltage of 25.5 volts gave an output of 11111111 (255 in binary), an input of 1.5 volts would give an output of 00001111 (15 in binary). For the control of something like an electric motor a digital to analogue to converter is required, and this works in the opposite way. In other words, if a digital input of 11111111 gave an output voltage of 25.5 volts, an input of 00001111 would give an output of 1.5 volts. There are actually logarithmic analogue to digital and digital to analogue converters, but most applications require linear types, and these are the only ones that are readily available to amateur users.

Both digital to analogue, and analogue to digital conversion involves a loss of accuracy. If we take an 8 bit converter of

74

either type, on the analogue side the circuit could be required to produce or convert an infinite range of voltages. However, on the digital side of the converter there are just 256 different levels. In our earlier example outputs at precisely 25.5 and 1.5 volts were available, but supposing 24.45 or 1.55 volts were needed. Neither of these could be achieved since the output increments in 0.1 volt steps, and it would be a matter of using the nearest output voltage and accepting an error of 0.05 volts.

For high accuracy a converter having a large number of bits is required, and in high quality audio applications, for instance, 14 or 16 bit converters are normally used. For something simple like a joystick input a 4 or 5 bit converter would probably be quite adequate. In our example above, outputs at 1.55 and 25.45 volts could be produced by using a 9 bit converter in place of an 8 bit type, doubling the number of available output voltages, and giving 0.05 volts increments. This would still not enable any desired voltage in the output range to be set precisely, but the maximum error would be reduced to just 0.025 volts. The larger the number of bits used, the greater the resolution and the better the attainable accuracy.

Most of the popular analogue converters are 8 bit types which are designed specifically for use with 8 bit microcomputers. It is possible to use a converter having more than 8 bits with a normal 8 bit home-micro, but the input to, or output from the converter, has to be taken in two separate bytes. Some simple mathematics in the computer is used to process the two received bytes to return the correct number, or process a number to send it out in two bytes. This is not normally necessary though, and although an 8 bit system may seem to offer only rather limited accuracy, results are adequate in this respect for many applications.

Suppose that the computer is to be used as a sophisticated model train controller, an 8 bit system would give stop plus 255 different speeds for the train. Even if one bit was used to set the direction of the train, this would still give stop plus 127 different speeds in each direction. This would in fact be more than adequate as each increment in speed would be only marginal. In practice there could well be no discernable difference between (say) speed 120 and speed 121.

Even on the measurement side 256 different levels is almost invariably quite adequate. This represents an accuracy of as little as 0.2% if a converter of suitably high quality is used, and this compares favourably with the accuracy obtained using even a large moving coil meter of high quality. It gives around ten times the accuracy obtained using a small panel meter of the type that are popular for home-contructor projects. Digital measuring equipment often uses a 3½ digit display, giving 1999 different display levels. In practice though, the real accuracy of such instruments falls well short of the theoretical maximum, and is often no better than about 0.5%. For absolute (rather than comparative) measurements the accuracy might well be no better than that provided by an 8 bit converter and a micro-computer.

Digital to Analogue

We will deal with digital to analogue conversion first as this is slightly more straightforward than analogue to digital conversion. There are several ways of achieving this type of conversion, but the system which is almost invariably used is one that is based on electronic switches and an $R - 2R$ resistor network. This system is outlined in Figure 28, which shows a four digit circuit. However, the system can obviously be extended or contracted to accommodate any desired number of bits.

The basic principle is quite simple, and if switch 3 is set to the high position the output of the voltage reference is fed to the output via the first of the "2R" resistors. There is a voltage drop through this resistor, but as it is feeding into a relatively high resistance (formed by a series — parallel combination of the other resistors) this voltage drop is not very large. If, on the other hand, switch 0 is set to the high position, there is a much higher resistance from the voltage reference to the output. Also, there are several shunt resistances of relatively low value, and only a small fraction of the reference voltage reaches the output. Setting two or more switches to the high state gives two or more paths from reference source to the output, and gives an output potential equal to the sum of the

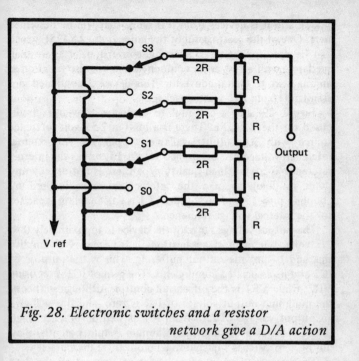

*Fig. 28. Electronic switches and a resistor
network give a D/A action*

voltages provided by each switch and its section of the resistor network.

Clearly switch 3 gives a larger boost in output voltage than switch 2, which in turn gives a larger boost in the output voltage than switch 1, and so on. It would take a lot of arithmetic to work out the output voltage for a given reference level, and at every combination of the switches, but this would in fact prove that the desired result is produced. If operating S0 boosted the output voltage by 1 volt, S1, S2 and S3 would boost it by 2, 4 and 8 volts respectively. A combination of (say) S0 and S2 would give an output voltage of 4 + 1 = 5 volts.

ZN425E

Ferranti produce an excellent range of analogue converters which are readily available to amateur users at reasonable prices, and it is devices from this range that will be described here. One of the most useful of the range is the ZN425E which can be used for digital to analogue conversion, or as we shall see later, with a few extra components it will also function as an analogue to digital converter. This device is contained in a standard 16 pin DIL plastic package.

Figure 29 shows a digital to analogue converter circuit based on the ZN425E. There is a built-in 2.55 volt reference source with its output available at pin 16. An external reference voltage can be applied to pin 15, but as the internal reference is a very high quality type there is not usually any point in doing so, and the internal reference is used by coupling pins 15 and 16 together. C1 is a decoupling capacitor for the internal voltage reference.

The output voltage range of the device is appoximately 0 to 2.5 volts, but in most applications it is necessary to amplify this and to provide output buffering. This is the purpose of IC2 and its associated components. The gain of IC2 is set using VR2, while VR1 is the offset null control. Although in theory the minimum output voltage of IC1 is zero, and this will give an output voltage of zero from IC2 as well, in practice small offset voltages occur and the minimum output potential may not be zero. VR1 is adjusted to trim out these inaccuracies.

The basic setting up procedure is to first set all the data inputs at zero and adjust VR1 for 0 volts at the output. With all the data inputs set high VR2 is then adjusted for the required maximum output potential. This whole procedure is repeated a few times until the desired accuracy is obtained.

Note that IC2 requires a −5 volt supply. This is needed to enable the output of IC2 to go right down to the 0 volt supply potential. Without this negative supply the minimum output voltage from IC2 would be about 2.5 volts above the 0 volt rail. Some computers have a suitable −5 volt output, but it is possible to derive one from the +5 volt supply if necessary. Ways of achieving this are described in the last part of this chapter.

VR2 can be adjusted for maximum output voltages of up to about 25 volts, but this is only possible if an adequate positive supply voltage is provided for IC2. This supply needs to be at

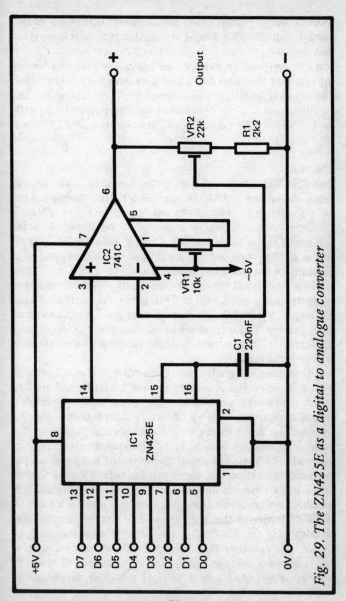

Fig. 29. The ZN425E as a digital to analogue converter

79

least 2 volts higher than the required maximum output voltage, but the total supply voltage for IC1 must not exceed 36 volts.

In high speed applications an important point to bear in mind is that the output of a digital to analogue converter does not respond instantly to a change on the data inputs. The "settling" time is the time taken for the output to go within 1 LSB of the correct level, and for the ZN425 this is typically $1\mu s$.

ZN426E

The ZN426E is a low current 8 bit digital to analogue converter. Whereas the ZN425E requires a typical supply current of 30 milliamps (40 milliamps maximum) the ZN426E consumes a typical supply current of 5 milliamps, with the maximum figure being just 9 milliamps. Like the ZN425E, it has a settling time of typically $1\mu s$. It is contained in a standard 14 pin DIL encapsulation.

Figure 30 shows the circuit diagram of a digital to analogue converter using the ZN426E. This device has an integral voltage reference with its output available at pin 6, but an external load resistor (R1) is required in addition to decoupling capacitor C1. This output is direct coupled to the reference voltage input at pin 5.

The output voltage is taken from pin 4, and is in the range 0 to 2.55 volts. IC2 is used to provide buffering and amplification, and in this case a CA3140E device is used. This has a class A output stage which enables its output terminal to swing almost right down to the negative supply rail potential. This enables satisfactory results to be obtained in many applications without having to resort to the use of a −5 volt supply for the device. However, where it is important for the output to go right down to the 0V rail potential, rather than just within a few millivolts of it, the output stage used in the circuit of Figure 29 should be employed. This output stage can be used with the ZN425E incidentally. As with the previous circuit, IC2 can only be powered from a +5 volt supply if a low maximum output voltage of only around 3 volts is required. For higher output voltages a positive supply rail at

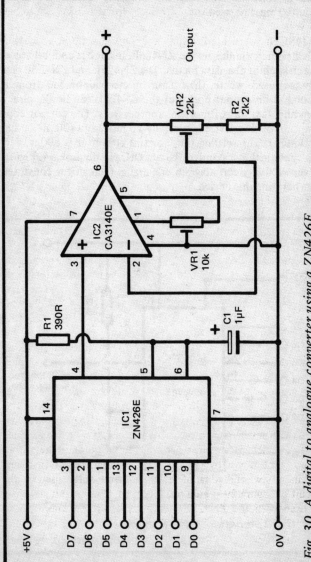

Fig. 30. A digital to analogue converter using a ZN426E

81

least 2 volts higher than the required maximum output potential must be used.

ZN428E
This device is similar to the ZN426E, but it has an 8 bit transparent latch at the data inputs. The ZN425E and ZN426E can only be used where their data inputs will be fed from a latching 8 bit output port, but the ZN428E can be fed direct from the data bus of most microprocessors. The current consumption of this device is typically 20 milliamps (30 milliamps maximum). The settling time for this converter is 800ns, and it is contained in a standard 16 pin DIL plastic package. Figure 31 shows the circuit diagram of a digital to analogue converter incorporating this device.

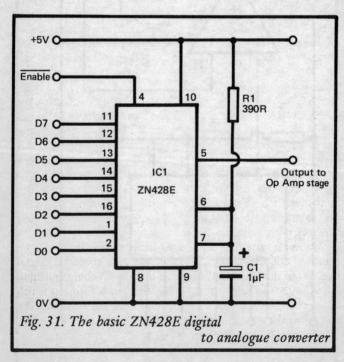

Fig. 31. The basic ZN428E digital
to analogue converter

R1 and C1 are the load resistor and decoupling capacitor for the internal 2.55 volt reference source, and the output of this is coupled to the reference input at pin 6. The analogue output is available at pin 5, and this would normally be taken to an amplifier/buffer stage, like those used in the two previous circuits.

The negative enable input at pin 4 controls the input latch, which is similar to the 74LS373 device which was briefly described earlier, but in this case the enable input operates in the opposite way. The latch is "transparent" when the enable input is taken low, and the latching action is produced when it is taken high. This terminal is therefore fed with the output of the address decoder circuit, and this must be a negative (low) pulse.

An unusual feature of the ZN428E is that it has separate digital and analogue earth terminals at pins 9 and 8 respectively. The device will operate properly with as much as plus or minus 0.2 volts between these two terminals, but in most cases they will simply be connected to a common earth rail.

Analogue to Digital

A digital to analogue converter can be used as the basis of an analogue to digital converter, and Figure 32 shows the usual approach to this. The inputs of the digital to analogue converter are fed from the output of a binary counter, and this is simply a circuit that starts with all its outputs low, and then counts up in binary fashion at a rate which is determined by a clock input signal. When it has counted up to the point where all the inputs are high, the next clock pulse takes it back to the original state with all outputs low, and it continues counting from the beginning again.

In this case the clock signal is obtained via a gate, and under stand-by conditions the gate will not pass the clock signal through to the counter. However, if the convert command input is fed with a suitable trigger pulse, this sets a flip/flop which enables the gate, and the counter commences operation. The inputs of the digital to analogue converter are fed from the binary counter's outputs, and this gives a stepped ramp output waveform. This rising voltage is compared with the input

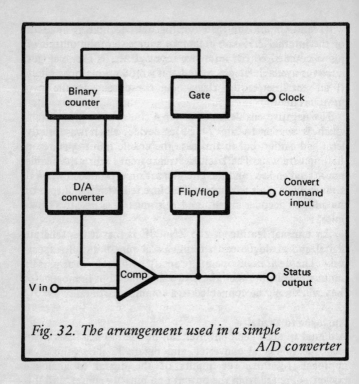

*Fig. 32. The arrangement used in a simple
A/D converter*

potential. Provided the input voltage is within the output
voltage range of the digital to analogue converter, the output
from the latter will eventually go above the input voltage. The
output of the comparator then changes state and resets the
flip/flop, cutting off the clock signal from the counter.

The higher the input voltage, the higher the number on the
outputs of the binary counter will become before the flip/
flop is reset and the count is "frozen". The output from the
counter therefore gives the required digital representation of the
input signal. The output of the comparator or the flip/flop
can be used as a status output to indicate to the computer
when a conversion has been completed. This is important for
two reasons, and one is that some form of syncronisation
between the computer and the converter is needed, as other-

wise the computer might read the converter during a conversion. The second reason is that an excessive input voltage will prevent the circuit from being reset and the conversion from being completed. The binary counter will just cycle indefinitely! If an input overload should occur the status output can be used to prevent the converter from being read and random numbers from being returned.

A disadvantage of this type of converter is that it is relatively slow. If an 8 bit converter using this system returned a value of 250, it would have taken 250 clock cycles for the conversion to be completed. With a clock frequency of (say) 250 kHz this would give a conversion time of 1ms. Lower input voltages would give a much faster conversion, but obviously such a fast conversion could not always be relied upon. Of course, for many applications high speed conversion is not important, and a converter which uses this system is perfectly suitable for non-critical applications.

Figure 33 shows a practical analogue to digital converter which uses this system, and is based on a ZN425E. While any digital to analogue converter can be used in this type of circuit, the ZN425E is much easier to use than most of the alternatives as it has a built-in binary counter, and it is designed for use in an analogue to digital converter circuit.

Pin 2 is the logic select input of IC1, and this is taken high by R1 so that the data pins plus the inputs of the digital to analogue converter are connected to the outputs of the binary counter.

IC2 is an operational amplifier, but it is used here as the comparator. R2 biases the non-inverting input to the negative supply rail and sets the input impedance of the circuit at 100k. However, the input impedance can be set at any figure within reason by giving R2 the appropriate value. The output of the digital to analogue converter is fed direct to the inverting input of IC2. When the output voltage of the converter exceeds the input voltage, the output of IC2 goes negative and resets the flip/flop which is formed by NAND gates IC3a and IC3b. IC3c is the clock control gate. The circuit operates with a clock frequency of up to 1MHz, and with most 6809 and 6502 systems a suitable clock signal will be available. With a micro-

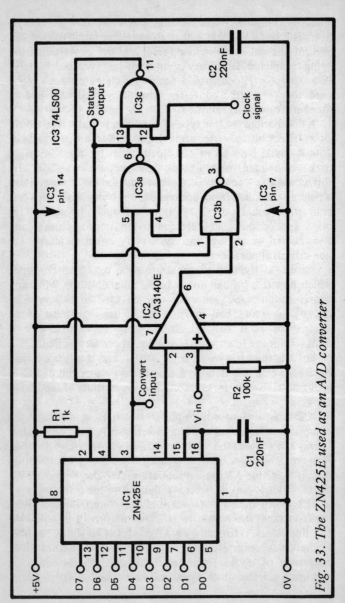

Fig. 33. The ZN425E used as an A/D converter

86

processor such as the Z80A the available clock frequency would amost certainly be too high, and it would then be necessary to divide the clock frequency by about four in order to obtain a suitably low frequency. Alternatively the converter could have its own clock oscillator operating at around 1MHz.

A negative pulse at the convert input sets the bistable so that the clock signal is restored to the binary counter again. This signal also resets the binary counter to zero. The status output is taken from the bistable circuit, and this goes high during a conversion (the output of IC3b is the complement of this). One gate of IC3 is left unused incidentally.

The eight outputs of the circuit do not have three state capability, and they must therefore be interfaced to the computer via an input port, not direct onto the data bus.

ZN427E

The ZN427E is an analogue to digital converter which uses a slightly different technique known as "successive approximation conversion". This is similar to the counting technique just described in that the output of a digital to analogue converter is compared with the input signal. The difference is that the digital input to the digital to analogue converter is compared and set one bit at a time, starting with the most significant bit.

The system works in the following fashion. All the bits are set to 0 apart from the most significant one, and the converted voltage is then compared with the input signal. If it is higher than the input signal the most significant bit is reset to zero, but if not it is left in the high state. Then the next bit is set to 1, and again, it is reset if the converted voltage is higher than the input potential, or left at 1 if it is not. This same procedure is carried out for the next six bits, one by one, with the digital output being set bit by bit to the correct number.

The point of this system is that it takes a consistent time for each conversion, and always a short time. In fact it takes just nine clock cycles, and the ZN427E has a maximum clock frequency of 600 kHz. This enables over 66000 conversions per second to be achieved.

Figure 34 shows a basic ZN427E analogue to digital

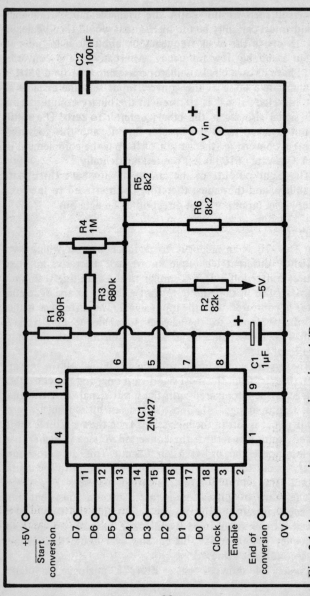

Fig. 34. A successive approximation A/D converter

88

converter circuit. An external clock oscillator is required, and a 1MHz clock signal from a 6502 or 6809 system is higher than the guaranteed maximum usable clock frequency of the device, although in most cases a 1MHz clock seems to be acceptable. However, a divider could be used to reduce an available clock frequency to a suitable figure, or a separate clock generator could be used for the device.

The outputs have three state capability, and the negative enable input at pin 2 is taken low to read the outputs (i.e. this is fed with a negative pulse from the address decoder circuit). The "start conversion" pulse is fed to pin 4, and a brief negative pulse is required here. It may be possible to drive this from a spare line on an output port, or another method that is often used is to feed this from an address decoder circuit so that PEEKing or POKEing a certain address starts a conversion. The "end of conversion" signal is available at pin 1. This goes low while a conversion is in progress and is high when the data on the outputs is valid.

R2 is the tail resistor for the fast comparator, and this requires a negative supply of between 3 and 30 volts. The specified value is for a −5 volt supply, and the value needed for a variety of other supply voltages is shown in the table provided below:

Voltage	Value
3 volts	47k
10 volts	150k
12 volts	180k
15 volts	220k
20 volts	330k
25 volts	390k
30 volts	470k

The current drawn from this negative supply is very low at around 65 microamps.

R3 to R5 are used to provide a zero adjustment and to set the input sensitivity (nominally 0 to 5 volts in this case), but the input circuit will probably need to be altered to suit the particular application in which the circuit is used.

The circuit of Figure 35 is for an analogue to digital con-

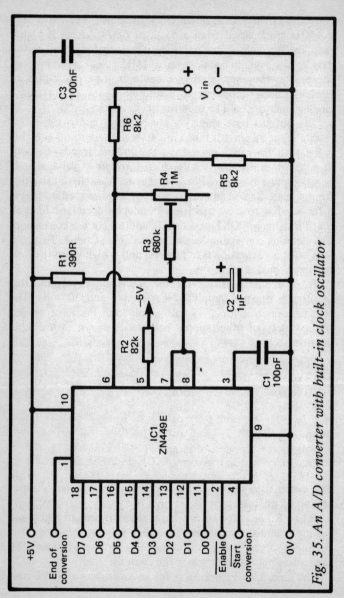

Fig. 35. An A/D converter with built-in clock oscillator

verter which uses a more recent device from Ferranti, the ZN449E. The circuit will also work with the ZN447E and ZN448E devices, which are identical to the ZN449E. The only difference is the degree of guaranteed accuracy that is obtained (¼ LSB for the ZN447E, ½ LSB for the ZN448E, and 1 LSB for the ZN449E). For most applications the ZN449E is satisfactory, but obviously one of the other two can be used in critical applications where their greater cost is justified.

The circuit is in many ways similar to the previous one, and the only major difference is that the ZN449E series have a built-in clock oscillator. This requires just one external capacitor (C1), and a value of 100pF sets the operating frequency at approximately 900 kHz. The maximum usable clock frequency is 1MHz, and if C1 is omitted an external clock signal can be applied to pin 3. However, in practice it is generally more convenient to use the internal clock with C1 set for a 900 kHz nominal clock frequency, which gives up to 1000000 conversions per second.

The ZN427E and the ZN449E series of devices all have a standard 18 pin DIL plastic encapsulation.

Negative Supply

As the negative supply for the two analogue to digital converters just described needs to have only a low potential and supply minimal current, it is quite easy to generate a suitable supply from a +5 volt supply. Figure 36 shows a simple way of doing this.

IC1a is an inverting Schmitt Trigger from a 74LS14 device, and together with R1 and C2 it forms a simple oscillator operating at a frequency of around 10 kHz. Its output is buffered by a second trigger of IC1, and then the output of this is rectified and smoothed by C2, D1, D2 and C3. This gives a loaded output voltage of approximately three volts, and a suitable tail resistor value for the ZN427E and ZN449E series when used with this circuit is 47k (see the table given earlier).

The circuit of Figure 36 is not very efficient, and it can only provide a very limited output current. Taking more than a few tens of microamps loads the output so heavily that the

91

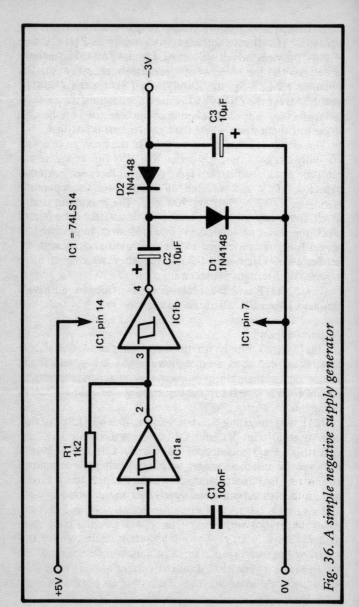

Fig. 36. A simple negative supply generator

92

supply voltage falls to practically zero. The ICL7660 is a useful device which provides a negative supply and gives a high level of efficiency. It actually gives a typical unloaded negative supply output of 99.9% of the positive input potential. The output voltage falls significantly when the negative output supply is loaded, with about 4.5 volts at 10 milliamps being obtained, and around 4 volts at 20 milliamps. The peak to peak ripple is typically 0.1 volts at an output current of 5 milliamps, and typically 0.2 volts with an output current of 20 milliamps.

While these figures may not be very impressive by normal power supply standards, in many applications the negative supply provided by this device is perfectly satisfactory. It is often very convenient to use the ICL7660 as it can enable an add-on to be powered solely from the computer where it would otherwise be necessary to build a mains power supply or use batteries to provide the negative supply rail.

Figure 37 shows the circuit for an ICL7660 used as a negative supply generator. The device is basically just a 10 kHz oscillator operating an electronic DPDT switch. C2 is first charged across the positive input supply, and then discharged (with the appropriate polarity) into C1, which is the smoothing capacitor at the negative output. C2 therefore transfers power from the positive supply to the negative one, and although the value of this component is not especially large, the high transfer frequency enables a reasonably output current to be drawn. In fact the main limiting factor on the available output voltage and current is the voltage drop that occurs through the electronic switches.

The ICL7660 is contained in a standard 8 pin DIL plastic package. An internal current limiting circuit prevents output currents of more than about 50 milliamps from being drawn, and protects the device against overloads on the output.

Analogue Multiplexer
The CMOS 4051BE analogue multiplexer/demultiplexer is a useful device when employed in conjunction with a digital to analogue or analogue to digital converter. Figure 38 shows the way in which this device is used.

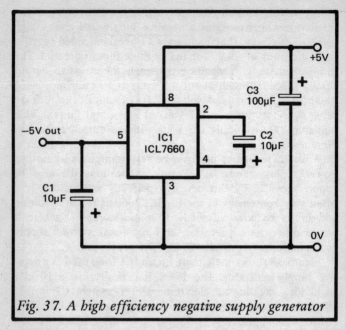

Fig. 37. A high efficiency negative supply generator

There are eight inputs and a single output. Which one of the inputs is connected through to the output depends on the address fed to the three address inputs, and these operate in standard binary fashion (e.g. A0, A1 and A2 all high selects input 7).

This device is not designed to handle logic signals, and is a true analogue device. Any voltage, provided it is between the two supply potentials, will be fed through to the output from the enabled input. There is a significant series resistance through the device, but as this is only in the region of 200 ohms it would not normally produce a significant voltage drop through the device, and is unlikely to be of any practical consequence.

One way in which the device can be used is to feed its output to the input of an analogue to digital converter. The three address lines can be fed from outputs of a latching port, and this enables any one of up to eight different input signals to be

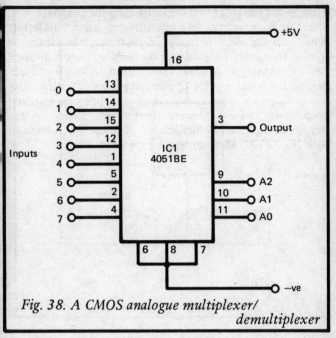

Fig. 38. A CMOS analogue multiplexer/
demultiplexer

selected and read under software control. This is much more simple and inexpensive than using eight analogue to digital converters, but it does have the slight disadvantage of effectively slowing down the conversion rate. With eight inputs to be converted in turn, each one can at most be read at one eighth of the converter's conversion rate. However, in many applications each input only needs to be read relatively infrequently, and an analogue multiplexer then represents the best solution to multiple analogue inputs.

The 4051BE is bilateral, and a signal fed to the output will be fed through to the appropriate input. It would therefore be possible to feed the output of a digital to analogue converter to any one of up to eight circuits under program control. As it would not be possible to maintain all eight outputs at once this would not be as useful as one might expect, although a sample and hold circuit could be used at each output to maintain the voltage between updates from the converter.

In this book we have been primarily concerned with getting signals into and out of a home-computer, and it is essential to become reasonably familiar with the basic techniques involved here before using a computer in even the most simple of applications. It is then possible to undertake more difficult control and measurement applications, using such things as light and temperature sensors, pulsed motor controllers, sound generators, and so on. Subjects of this type are covered in Book No. BP131, *Micro Interfacing Circuits – Book 2.*

Notes

Notes

Notes

OTHER BOOKS OF INTEREST

BP131: MICRO INTERFACING CIRCUITS – BOOK 2
R. A. Penfold
This book is intended to carry on from where Book 1 left off, and where the latter is principally concerned with getting signals into and out of a microcomputer, this publication is primarily about practical applications beyond the parallel or serial interface to the microprocessor. In other words, it is about so-called "real world" interfacing, including such topics as sound generators, speech generators, motor controllers, temperature sensors, optical sensors, etc. Like *Micro Interfacing Circuits – Book 1*, this publication does not treat the subject in a purely theoretical manner, or even in a largely theoretical way. Practical circuits using real rather than imaginary devices are provided, together with detailed circuit descriptions and any relevant background information, so that anyone with a reasonable knowledge of electronics should have no difficulty in using these circuits, adapting them slightly, where necessary, to suit their particular applications. In many cases a near beginner to electronics should have no real difficulty in using the circuits, but this book is not intended for complete beginners.

112 pages   *1984*
0 85934 106 2   **£2.75**

BP124: EASY ADD-ON PROJECTS FOR SPECTRUM, ZX81 & ACE
O. Bishop
This book describes how to build a number of electronic projects which you can use with your Spectrum, ZX81 or Jupiter Ace microcomputer.

The projects include a Pulse Detector, Picture Digitiser, Five-key Pad, Model Controller, Bleeper, Lamp Flasher, Light Pen, Magnetic Catch, Lap Sensor, Photo-flash, Games Control and six more projects that make up a Weather Station.

All the projects are fairly simple and inexpensive to construct. The most complicated part, the Address Decoder, is constructed as a separate item that can then be used with any of the projects.

Once built, the projects are easy to operate and a simple program or two is included to get you started. Of course, those readers who are more experienced at programming can have a lot of fun in writing elaborate programs for these projects, but the beginner can start with a short program and perhaps add extra features later.

192 pages   *1983*
0 85934 099 6   **£2.95**

Please note following is a list of other titles that are available in our range of Radio, Electronics and Computer Books.

These should be available from all good Booksellers, Radio Component Dealers and Mail Order Companies.

However, should you experience difficulty in obtaining any title in your area, then please write directly to the publisher enclosing payment to cover the cost of the book plus adequate postage.

If you would like a complete catalogue of our entire range of Radio, Electronics and Computer Books then please send a Stamped Addressed Envelope to:

BERNARD BABANI (publishing) LTD
THE GRAMPIANS
SHEPHERDS BUSH ROAD
LONDON W6 7NF
ENGLAND